EXPLORING LA
Rocks & Land

The Cumberland Geological Society

Foreword by
Sir Chris Bonington MBE

Edited by

Susan Beale
and
Mervyn Dodd

Published by
The Cumberland Geological Society
Quinta
Grizebeck
Kirby-in-Furness
Cumbria LA17 7XJ

www.cumberland-geol-soc.org.uk

Designed, printed and bound by
Printexpress Unit 1 Sneckyeat Road Industrial Estate,
Hensingham, Whitehaven, Cumbria. CA28 8PF
Tel: 01946-66081 Fax 01946-66315
E-mail: sales@printex.co.uk

British Library

ISBN 978-0-9558453

CONTENTS

"Exploring Lakeland Rocks and Landscapes"

Foreword

I first visited the Lakes as a child during the Second World War and have lived and climbed amongst its hills for the last forty five years. I have come to love the fells of the Lake District and to recognise that there is nowhere in the world that is more beautiful. There is a perfection in the compact pattern of valleys, lakes and mountain ridges, clad in grass, heather and forest of so many different tones of green and brown and purple.

There have been many changes since my first visit - more visitors and consequently more traffic and greater foot erosion on the fells, demanding man made foot paths that have been made in an aesthetically pleasing way from local stones manhandled into place. Indeed the Lakes have been affected by the hands of man for several thousand years, from early clearings in the valley in Neolithic times, the building of farms and cottages through the ages, the felling of trees for farm land in the valleys and the wooden walls of Britain's navy in the 18th century, quarrying from a very early period and of course the grazing of sheep that enable us to walk so easily across the fell. Thanks to its National Park status in recent years, the hand of man, on the whole, has been sensitive and the Lakeland farms, cottages and dry stone walls supplement rather than detract from the beauty of the hills.

Yet all these changes are superficial when you look at the hills, rocky crags, soaring ridges and glaciated valleys that have been formed over thousands of years and have hardly changed in the tiny span of time in geological terms that man has had an impact. I hope this book helps the reader have a deeper understanding of how this very special corner of England has been formed, and through that get an even greater appreciation of its natural beauty.

Chris Bonington
5 February 2008

PREFACE

This book is for all who want to truly explore Lakeland.   For those who when they are out walking would like to understand how the fascinating rocks and landscapes of Lakeland have formed. It is for the enquiring, the curious, the appreciative residents and visitors who want to know when and how it all happened.   You don't need to have a good knowledge of Earth Sciences to be comfortable using this book. Interested amateurs will find much to interest them, and professionals may be introduced to aspects or localities which enhance their knowledge.

We begin with an introductory chapter which sets the scene for the individual excursion chapters and tells the fantastic story how the rocks and scenery of Lakeland have evolved.   There are 17 walks, ranging from Carrock Fell in the north to Arnside on Morecambe Bay in the south and from St. Bees in the west to the Pennine edge in the east.   The walks include easy, half day lowland routes as well as all day demanding routes on the fellsides. Each chapter is self contained and all have been walked by volunteers to check rigorously the accuracy of our route-finding instructions.   Details of parking locations are given.   The Glossary gives brief explanations of terms that appear in bold in the text. Up to date details of museums and how to contact them are provided together with other sources of further information.

We hope this book will enhance your enjoyment of the lovely landscapes of Lakeland and its surrounding area, one of the jewels of the English countryside.   Please help to maintain and conserve them.   At a practical level, please drive carefully, park vehicles considerately, close farm gates and don't leave any litter!

ACKNOWLEDGEMENTS

We gratefully appreciate the advice, encouragement and hard work of the Steering Group: Margaret Bennett, Ann Freeland, David Powell, Judy Suddaby and Rosemary Vidler. The seventeen authors have been most helpful and forbearing with the many requests we have made and we thank them for their constructive help.

Producing this book has involved the active support of many members and friends of the Society including those who so willingly trial walked the excursions, proof read the scripts, and Council Members for their enthusiasm for this enterprise. Many thanks to Dr Alan Smith for his painstaking and brisk proof reading.

We have benefited from advice from officers of the British Geological Survey and many others who have answered our queries with unstinting generosity of time and we gratefully acknowledge the financial support of the following sponsors:

Hanson Aggregates
Tendley Quarries Limited
Friends of the Lake District
Keswick and District Neighbourhood Forum
Awards for All
The Curry Fund of the Geologists' Association
Carlisle City Council Community Support
Cumberland Pencil Company
Maryport Cooperative Society

Note. The routes followed are almost entirely on public rights of way. Please seek permission beforehand on the rare occasions it is necessary to cross private land.

Please heed the notes on safety given in the excursion chapters. Neither the Cumberland Geological Society nor the individual authors can take responsibility for accidents or injuries sustained on these walks. We advise you to take with you an appropriate map, particularly the OS Explorer 1:25 000 sheet. On upland walks please carry a compass and know how to use it. A GPS would be a bonus. Before a walk on high ground, remember to check the weather forecast and please remember that conditions can change very quickly, so be prepared.

Front Cover photograph: Blackmoss Pot, Langstrath.
Photo F. Lawton

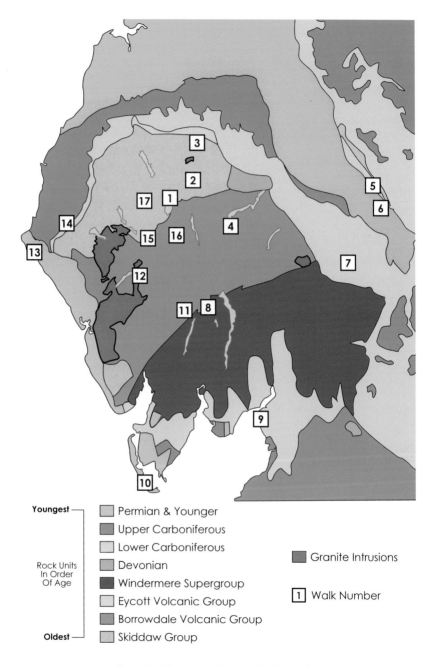

Figure i. Geological map of Lakeland.

8

INTRODUCTION

The story of Cumbria begins about 480**Ma** [1](million years ago) early in the Ordovician Period (see Figure ii), near a small continent called Avalonia, which lay in high latitudes in the Southern Hemisphere (see Figure iii). Life had already evolved in the sea but there was very little if any vegetation or animal life on land. Avalonia was therefore subject to quite rapid erosion. Periodic storms carried sediments into the ocean to the north, where muds and sands were deposited, building up a great thickness of sediments. These were eventually **lithified** to become the oldest rocks in the Lake District – the Skiddaw Group – which form the smoother hills of the Northern Fells (Skiddaw, Blencathra) and of Black Combe.

Avalonia was part of a **tectonic plate** (an extensive, rigid mass of continental and oceanic crust) which gradually moved north overriding the adjacent tectonic plate, Baltica, causing the southern edge of the latter to be **subducted**. The subduction resulted in volcanic activity about 460Ma which formed an island arc, perhaps like present day Japan.

The lava erupted relatively quietly, rather like the volcanoes of present day Hawaii, and a series of lava flows built up a great thickness. These flows cooled and solidified and now form the Eycott Volcanic rocks in northeast Lakeland.

As the tectonic plate continued to move northwards the centre of volcanic activity moved to the land where more relatively quiet lava flows built up another thick sequence. We recognise these flows in the lower part of the Borrowdale Volcanic Group, which can be seen spectacularly in St. John's in the Vale where each lava flow is now a tough rock which resists erosion and stands proud as a cliff edge partway up the hillside.

---

1 terms in heavy bold print are explained in the Glossary at the end of the book.

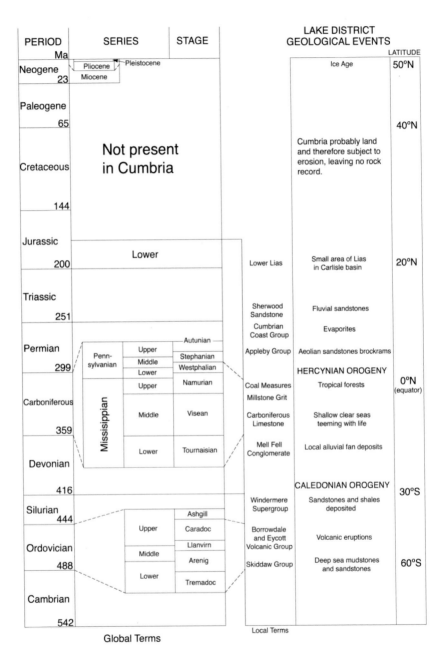

PERIOD Ma	SERIES		STAGE	LAKE DISTRICT GEOLOGICAL EVENTS		LATITUDE
Neogene 23	Pliocene Miocene		Pleistocene		Ice Age	50°N
Paleogene 65						40°N
Cretaceous 144	**Not present in Cumbria**				Cumbria probably land and therefore subject to erosion, leaving no rock record.	
Jurassic 200	Lower			Lower Lias	Small area of Lias in Carlisle basin	20°N
Triassic 251				Sherwood Sandstone	Fluvial sandstones	
				Cumbrian Coast Group	Evaporites	
Permian 299	Penn- sylvanian	Upper	Autunian	Appleby Group	Aeolian sandstones brockrams	
		Middle	Stephanian		HERCYNIAN OROGENY	0°N (equator)
		Lower	Westphalian			
Carboniferous 359	Missisippian	Upper	Namurian	Coal Measures	Tropical forests	
				Millstone Grit		
		Middle	Visean	Carboniferous Limestone	Shallow clear seas teeming with life	
		Lower	Tournaisian	Mell Fell Conglomerate	Local alluvial fan deposits	
Devonian 416					CALEDONIAN OROGENY	30°S
Silurian 444			Ashgill	Windermere Supergroup	Sandstones and shales deposited	
	Upper		Caradoc	Borrowdale and Eycott Volcanic Group	Volcanic eruptions	
Ordovician 488	Middle		Llanvirn			
			Arenig	Skiddaw Group	Deep sea mudstones and sandstones	60°S
	Lower		Tremadoc			
Cambrian 542						

Global Terms   Local Terms

Figure ii. Stratigraphical Table.

The relatively quiet lava flows were succeeded by much more explosive eruptions, probably like those which erupted in 1988 in Mt. St Helens in the USA. They formed huge mountains with immense **calderas,** the remnants of which form the rugged rocks of the central fells. (Walk No. 15 explores this country). All this volcanic activity took place over a period of about 5 million years between 460Ma and 450Ma. It was succeeded by a much quieter period when there was no volcanic activity and the huge mountains which had been built up, were eroded away.

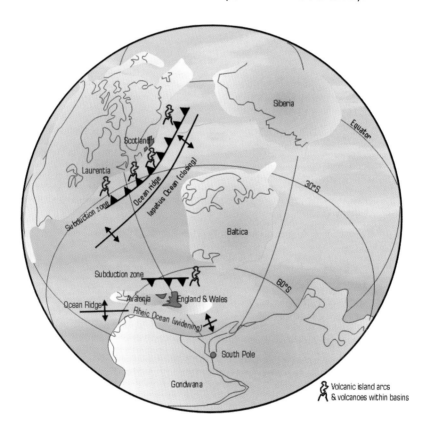

Figure iii. Global Palaeogeography in Arenig times, (485-470Ma).
From P Toghill, Geology of Shropshire, Crowood Press 2006.
Fig. 66, p. 86, with permission.

While erosion was occurring at the surface of the earth, at very deep levels at the base of the Earth's crust, there was partial melting of the mantle, which caused a vast magma chamber to be formed. Magma from this chamber was pushed up into the crust where it slowly cooled, still at a depth of several kilometres. We meet this cooled magma when, much later, it is exposed on the surface of the earth and forms the intrusive rocks e.g. of Ennerdale Granophyre, Eskdale Granite, (Walk 12), Skiddaw Granite (Walk 2) and the various rocks of Carrock Fell (Walk 3).

About 430Ma in Silurian times, the sea advanced to cover the whole of our area, which by then was heavily eroded, laying down thick sediments of mud and sand, some rich enough in marine animals for the shells to form thin limestones. These sediments were in due course lithified to form the various rocks of the Windermere Supergroup which are visited in Walk 8.

Our tectonic plate, having joined Baltica, continued its journey across the globe and collided with a third tectonic plate carrying Laurentia (which would later become North America). All these movements are slow – continents probably moving then at the same rate they are now, i.e. a few centimetres a year. The collision caused a huge mountain building event (the Caledonian **orogeny**) which folded the rocks to form a high mountain range, similar in size to the present day Alps, across what would become North West Europe and North East America. This very major event compressed and folded all the rocks which we have been describing. In particular the original muds and sands of the Skiddaw Group were folded, refolded and compressed making them difficult to understand. Some of the muds were deformed so much that they became Skiddaw slates. This orogeny also altered the volcanic deposits, particularly the ash falls, compressing them to form the well known Honister slates. Some of the lava flows were more resistant to the pressures and were only slightly tilted, as can be seen in St. John's in the Vale and above Derwentwater.

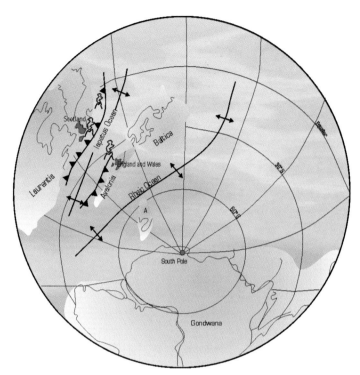

Figure iv. Global palaeogeography in Caradoc times (458-449Ma)
From P Toghill, Geology of Shropshire, Crowood Press 2006.
Fig. 67, p. 88, with permission.

By this time Avalonia was part of a bigger continent situated just south of the equator.   The major mountain range formed by the Caledonian Orogeny was now exposed to rapid erosion in a desert environment.   Some of the sediments from this erosion are preserved in Great and Little Mell Fell.   By 360Ma the mighty mountains had been eroded down to sea level and most of the area that would become southern Britain was covered by a warm shallow sea in which flourished a wide range of animals.   The shells of many, many millions of animals accumulated on the seafloor in shallow marine basins.   These basins slowly subsided allowing the continued build up of shells until the huge thicknesses we call the Carboniferous Limestones were formed.   Walk 9 visits these rocks near Morecambe Bay and Walk 7 their landscapes near Shap.

Rivers from a landmass to the north brought down huge volumes of sediment, which built up on the shallow seafloor and eventually supported the luxuriant exotic forests of the Carboniferous Period. The trees and other vegetation of these forests accumulated as great thicknesses of sediments which changed after they had been buried and compressed to form valuable coalfields. These Carboniferous rocks of limestones, sandstones, shales and coal form an extensive but discontinuous ring around the Lake District (see Figure i).

Our tectonic plate continued to move and eventually all the landmasses were assembled to form the huge supercontinent of Pangea straddling the equator, with "Britain" surrounded by land and experiencing a hot arid climate. These uplands were eroded by flash floods to form the Permian **brockrams** or **breccias** which are now found in the Vale of Eden (Walk 6). Along with red (desert) shales, sandstones and evaporates which are normally highly soluble salts, these coarse sediments were laid down between 300 and 250Ma but dating of these particular rocks is so very difficult due to the lack of fossils. During the succeeding Triassic Period (250-200Ma) conditions were very similar – Walk 13 visits these. The Triassic is the last Period with extensive outcrops in Cumbria.

From this time (c200Ma) forward until near the end of the Great Ice Age there is virtually no record in the Cumbrian rock sequence. Sediments were almost certainly deposited but were removed by erosion. During this 200 million year interval the Atlantic Ocean has opened and the plate carrying Britain had travelled north to reach its present position.

The Cumbrian landscape was significantly modified during the Quarternary Period (2.6Ma to 10 000**BP**). This was the time of the Great Ice Age, a time of multiple ice advances and intervening warmer **interglacials**. The last main ice advance was the late Devensian (26 000-13 000BP)[2] the effects of which dominate

---

2   These dates are constantly being reviewed.

present day relief.   Glacial erosion, mainly by valley glaciers but also in part by temporary icecaps covering Cumbria, was the major process in the Lake District fells.   The main valleys were overdeepened, but with long, narrow, ribbon lakes like Coniston filling their basins.

Valley sides were straightened with the spurs or ridges separating tributary streams being trimmed off by moving ice.   Tributary valley floors now "hang" high above the main valleys.   Many of these tributary streams now rise in **corries**, deep armchair shaped hollows, excavated by valley glaciers.   The corries are flanked by **arêtes**, narrow knife edge ridges like Striding Edge, formed when adjacent valleys were deeply eroded.   Walk 4 in the Ullswater area and Walk 11 at Tilberthwaite visits such features. **Moraines**, other glacial **drift** and meltwater landforms are much smaller scale features of the valleys.   Walk 1 beside Derwentwater, looks at these features, which are mentioned in other walks.

The Cumbrian lowlands, especially north and west of the Lake District, where there are thick layers of drift or **till**, have been mainly influenced by glacial depositon.   **Drumlins**, long, low, blunt-ended hills of glacial drift sweep round from the Vale of Eden through the Carlisle Plain into West Cumbria, reflecting the direction of movement of ice sheets.   Rather featureless masses of sand and gravel, laid down by meltwater from the ice, cover large stretches of the lowlands. Stream courses have been disrupted by diversions of drainage due to ice, the best known being the diversion of the River Derwent at the foot of Bassenthwaite.   Walk 10 on Walney Island and Walk 13 at St Bees visit such landscapes.

Appropriately we are deeply concerned by the prospect of global warming due to man's activities, yet there remains the very real prospect of another major ice advance, but not in our lifetime.

Walk Number 1

Keswick Landscapes

by Margaret Bennett

Purpose   To look at glacial features in the landscape near Derwentwater.

Practical Details

Starting Point   Car park by The Theatre by the Lake, Keswick.

Walk Description   6-8 km easy, low level walk on good paths.

Maps   1:25 000 OL4 The English Lakes North Western area.
1:50 000 Landranger sheets 89 or 90.

Public Transport   Bus to Keswick bus station.

Public Toilets   Car park at beginning of walk.

Refreshments   Snacks available at Theatre by the Lake. Many cafes in Keswick.

GEOLOGICAL BACKGROUND

The Borrowdale Valley was excavated by ice in rocks of Ordovician age, the older Skiddaw Group to the north and west and the younger Borrowdale Volcanic Group in the south and east. The evidence of the most recent ice advances falls into two groups. One group of landforms is due to advancing ice moving down the valley. The second group of landforms is deposits formed as the ice retreated or wasted away. The advancing ice excavated the lake basin and deposited **drumlins**. The retreating ice left behind landforms best seen around Calfclose Bay.

EXCURSION DETAILS

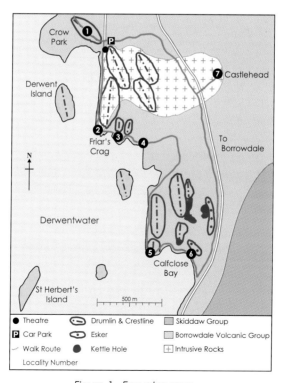

Figure 1. Excursion map.

Crow Park is across Lake Road from the car park (NY 265 229). Enter by the low gate nearest to the Theatre and walk to the crest of the low hill (300m). This, **Locality 1** (NY 265 230), is a drumlin, a long, low, rounded, streamlined oval mound, locally aligned southeast to northwest along the direction of ice movement Drumlins probably formed when moving ice, moulded subglacial material of various origins, shapes and sizes. Lord's Island and Derwent Isle, are partially submerged drumlins. From this vantage point you can look up Derwent Water with its lush wooded shores, to the Jaws of Borrowdale, where the valley narrows as it enters the Borrowdale Volcanic Group outcrop. The whole of the western shore is on the Skiddaw Group Rocks (Ordovician 475 - 460 **Ma**). The eastern shore from about halfway down the lake is on Borrowdale Volcanic Group rocks (460 - 450 Ma).

Leave Crow Park by the gate you entered. Follow the path for about 800m to the end of Friar's Crag, See Figure 2. This crag is **Locality 2** (NY264 223), and is thought to be named after the 8th Century Saint Herbert, who lived on St. Herbert's Island in the lake. This crag is where his followers stood by the lake and received his blessing. The crag is part of a diorite **intrusion** which can be seen quite clearly at the end of the viewpoint, though it is badly weathered and, in places, covered in lichen. It is a fine-grained igneous rock, rich in iron and magnesium which gives the rock its dark colour. The contact between the intrusion and Skiddaw Group rocks can sometimes be traced just above the high-water line. The intrusion resisted erosion more than the surrounding rock, and may form the core of a drumlin, with the up-valley end eroded by the lake. This feature is known as a crag and tail, with a steep slope up valley, but a gentle slope down valley where deposited material remains. The intrusion also outcrops in Cockshot Wood and north of Friar's Crag where again it forms the core of drumlins, and on Castle Head across the Borrowdale Road.

Figure 2. Friar's Crag from Derwentwater.
(Photo F. Lawton)

Follow the pathway down the steps to **Locality 3,** Strandshag Bay, (NY 265 222), where there are two smaller drumlins. Climb one of them to examine their shape and orientation. The more northerly one appears to be superimposed on the flank of the larger drumlin formed in Cockshot Wood and may represent a later, lower energy ice advance. Continue along the path round the edge of the bay into the Ings, a wooded marshy area.

Locality 4 is the delta of Brockle Beck, (NY 268 222), an area where the stream banks reveal bedding in the sand and gravel indicating these were deposited by water, not ice. When you leave the woodland, turn west along the foot of a drumlin to Stable Hills. Here there is an exposure of glacial **till** along the lakeside in a long low drumlin just south of Stable Hills. There are stiles and steps down to the lakeshore where you can see close up the erosion by lake waves.

Continue along the path, following a sign to Calfclose Bay.
Locality 5, (NY 267 216), is Broomhill Point at the end of Calfclose Bay, a small wooded area with a large seat overlooking the lake. Broomhill Point is the eroded end of a drumlin. The interior of the drumlin is bouldery till which can be seen from the lakeshore. At this point it is possible to work out that ice moved from south to north. The evidence is the parallel lines of drumlin crests and the orientation of elongated stones in the clayey till lying lengthways along the direction of movement of the ice. The till is tough and difficult to loosen, particularly between 1 m and 0-5 m below the surface. This compaction probably resulted from freeze/thaw, tundra-like conditions during and after the last main glacial episode. This compacted horizon is known as **fragipan,** in which drainage and root penetration are difficult.

As you leave Broomhill Point to continue around Calfclose Bay, a piece of modern sculpture in the form of a large, split boulder, can be seen by the water's edge (NY 268 215). It commemorates the first hundred years of the National Trust, and is cut into a large boulder of **andesitic** lava from the upper Borrowdale Valley. Beside the path there is a dedication plaque made from a piece of fine-grained ash-fall **tuff.**

Follow the path alongside Calfclose Bay. **Locality 6** (NY 268 214), is a low ridge to your left. Material in the banks of the stream show that it consists mainly of sand and gravel. It is better sorted, better bedded and less compacted than the clayey till of Broomhill Point. This is just one of a number of **eskers** in this vicinity, long, narrow ridges of sand and gravel deposited by melt water streams in, under or alongside the ice. The depressions to the west, with reeds growing through the grass and often wooded, are **kettle holes**. These probably formed when large blocks of ice, trapped in glacial sediment, eventually melted, leaving hollows. The rounded hill, crowned with five oak trees, in the field next to the lake, is a **kame.** This consists of sand and gravel probably laid down on top of the ice.

About halfway round the bay take the northeast (left) fork. Where the path approaches the main Borrowdale road there is a bus stop and the National Trust's Great Wood car park. Follow this path beside the Borrowdale road back towards Keswick. Several eskers can be seen in the field between the road and the lake. Continue along this path until you reach the turning to Cockshot Wood. At this point carefully cross the road and follow the steep path up Castle Head. This is the main outcrop of the intrusion seen at Friar's Crag. From its top, **Locality 7,** (NY 269 227), there is an overview of the glaciated landscape with its contrasting eskers and drumlins. It is also a good vantage point to compare the Skiddaw Group rocks with the Borrowdale Volcanic Group rocks. To the north & west, the Skiddaw rocks are mainly mudstones with the occasional sandstone bed. These rocks form screes at the foot of hills and produce fells with rounded outlines. Most of the larger screes date from the most recent ice advance. The Borrowdale Volcanic Group rocks to the south and east are resistant to erosion, lavas forming the cliffs and tuffs the gentler slopes. Castle Head also exhibits the crag and tail topography seen at Friar's Crag. From Castle Head you can see how the tributary valley from Watendlath 'hangs' high above Borrowdale, the Watendlath Beck tumbling over Lodore Falls. The thicker ice in the main valley excavated much more deeply than the thinner ice in the Watendlath valley.

Return to the road along the path. Cross the road and follow the sign posted track between fields to Cockshot Wood, turning north northwest back to the car park.

Walk Number 2

Glenderaterra Valley

by Rosemary Vidler

Purpose	To look at the Skiddaw Granite exposure in Sinen Gill and to see how the surrounding rocks of the Skiddaw Group have been thermally metamorphosed.

Practical Details

Starting point	Car park just above the Blencathra Centre (NY 302 257).
Walk description	Hard – an all day excursion of about 7 km. over rough open fell side rising to approx. 500m.
Map	1:25 000 OL4 The English Lakes North western area.
Public transport	Buses from Keswick and Penrith to Threlkeld village. It is a 2 km walk from the bus stop to the Blencathra Centre.
Public toilets	In the village behind the Public Room (NY 320 254).
Refreshments	There are two Pubs in the village serving food and the Post Office is open Tuesdays and Thursdays selling sweets and drinks.

GEOLOGICAL SETTING

Within the Skiddaw Group rocks of this area there are three small outcrops of **Skiddaw Granite**, which are set in an **aureole** of darker **thermally metamorphosed** mudstones and **greywackes**, (see Figure 1). This area of altered rocks covers approximately 70km². The current excursion is to the small southern outcrop at Sinen Gill on the western flank of Blencathra.

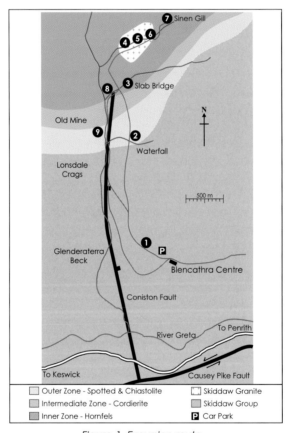

Figure 1. Excursion route.

The Skiddaw Granite has been intruded into **sedimentary** rocks of the Skiddaw group and gravity evidence suggests that this intrusion is relatively flat topped and steep sided (a stock) and elongated in a Northeast to Southwest direction. It is part of the large granite mass **(batholith)** that lies under the Lake District and the Northern Pennines. Radiometric age determination of the Skiddaw Granite gives a mean age of 397±2 Ma. This suggests intrusion occurred during the Silurian or early Devonian, almost at the end of the Caledonian Orogeny. The Caledonian Orogeny was a period of mountain building that occurred when the continents of North America and Scandinavia collided and Scotland became attached to Britain, (see main introduction). The effects of this collision can be seen in the **regionally metamorphosed** rocks of the Skiddaw Group, which were altered by heating and deformation on a massive scale.

As you get closer to the granite the thermal metamorphic features become easier to recognise. The rocks become much harder and the faint spots become more obvious as dark black spots of cordierite (an aluminium silicate mineral formed when clays are heated by thermal metamorphism). Close to the granite itself these spotted rocks also show a pitchy sheen and the spots of cordierite are much darker. These features suggest that this granite was never at very high temperatures when it was intruded. If it had been hotter different minerals would have appeared in the rock and the county rock would be more altered. The granite itself consists of interlocking crystals of white rectangular **feldspar,** a dark platy iron rich mineral **(biotite)** and glassy grey **quartz.**

The Glenderaterra valley follows the line of the Coniston **Fault** that extends into the Southern Lakes (Figure1). The northern part of the fault is displaced westwards from the Vale of St John's by another fault, the Causey Pike Fault, which the A66 follows between Penrith and Keswick. There is extensive mineralization in the valley along the faults and **joint** planes and the lead and copper ores found there have been exploited.

EXCURSION DESCRIPTION

Localities 1 – 7 examine the increasing effects of thermal metamorphism as the granite contact is approached. There is an optional extension to localities 8 and 9 to explore the exploitation of mineralised veins.

Start at the car park above the Blencathra Centre (NY 302 257) and head northwest along the rough track.

Locality 1 is 75 metres from the car park. As you move along the track, 15m above to the north are exposures of blue grey Skiddaw Group mudstones. These have been hardened by **regional** not thermal **metamorphism**. As you follow the track round and start heading up the valley you may find faint grey spotting in the rocks due to thermal metamorphism.

Locality 2 (NY 299 270) is at the first gill below a waterfall. There is much reddening of the rock from iron staining by **hematite**. It is possible that this gill follows the line of a fault and the fracturing of the rock has allowed hematite mineralization. Some small specimens of iron ore (kidney ore) have been found here. More noticeable are the spectacular, needle-like, white chiastolite crystals (a form of aluminium silicate) in the rock, formed by more intense thermal metamorphism. Please do not hammer the rock; there are usually plenty of fragments to examine. Then continue along the track to the bridge at Roughten Gill.

Locality 3 (NY 298 276) is at Roughten Bridge. This bridge is made of flat slabs of hardened mudstone (**hornfels**) with spots of dark cordierite in them, better seen in the supporting structures. These formed as a result of increasing temperatures closer to the granite. At one edge of the bridge is a 'misfit', a slab of green volcanic rock probably brought up from Borrowdale to help finish the bridge.

The hornfels slabs ring if tapped *gently* with a hammer. Please be careful not to damage the stones. Keswick Museum houses the famous "Skiddaw Musical Stones". These are a xylophone like arrangement of these hornfels stones on which tunes can be played. From here follow the south bank of Sinen Gill for about 450m (no path) uphill to Locality 4.

Locality 4 (NY 299 278) is an area of steep bare ground on the south side of the stream. Down by the stream there is a large boulder of granite and about 3m east at the bottom of the bank an outcrop that has been heavily weathered and reduced to what looks like coarse white grit. This is decomposed granite. Acids in the peat probably attacked the feldspars in the granite, accelerating decomposition. Continue upstream about 100m to a prominent waterfall.

Locality 5 (NY 300 281) is this waterfall, about 2 metres high. The granite around it is strongly jointed. The joints formed when the hot granite cooled and contracted. Continue upstream for another 100m.

Locality 6 (NY 301 281) is a small waterfall at the foot of which the contact between the granite and the hornfels can be seen on the northern bank of the stream. This dips gently to the east. If you carefully cross the stream and look closely at the contact you can see the weathered granite and on top of it darkly spotted hornfels with a thin quartz vein between.

Cross the stream carefully to the north side above the waterfall and move up 300m towards Locality 7. 70m beyond Locality 6 and 30-40 metres north from the stream there are exposures of hornfelsed greywacke with small scale folding on west facing rocks (see Figure 2).

Figure 2. Folding in hornfelsed greywacke.   Cleavage is also visible.
(Photo R. Vidler)

Locality 7 (NY 304 283) is near a ruined sheepfold by the stream. 50m before reaching the sheepfold are more exposures of folded greywacke (see Figure 2).

This is the end of this part of the excursion and you should return downstream to the track and make your way back to the car park.

Returning along the track notice in the valley bottom the remains of the workings of the Glenderaterra Mine. These mines were worked from 1872-1920. They produced **galena** (lead ore) and **chalcopyrite** (a copper ore). There are some old levels to be seen on the eastern bank with other workings on the west bank. If you wish you could drop down to have a look at these at localities 8 and 9. The ground can be very wet and boggy and there is no path.

Locality 8 (NY 296 275) is where Roughten Gill meets the main beck. Here is a vein where samples of quartz, **barite** (a barium sulphate mineral) and green **malachite** (a copper mineral) can be found. If Roughten Gill can be crossed two collapsed levels can be seen further downstream. These were the older workings. Glenderaterra Beck itself can be difficult to cross if there is a lot of water. If you cross to the main workings at *Locality 9* (NY 297 273). Please take great care, as there is a flooded open shaft. Specimens of heavy, grey galena can be found. This has a silvery sheen when freshly broken. The heavy white mineral is barite and the glassy mineral is quartz.

Cross back over the river and follow the old mine track downstream. Before cutting steeply up the fell side to rejoin the upper track to the car park you may be able to see the remains of a water wheel pit in the valley bottom. This was used to pump water out of one of the shafts.

Alternatively you can continue along the old mine track to where it passes through a gate to join a tarmac road. Take the footpath immediately on the left (east) over a stile and make your way uphill back to the Blencathra Centre. Continue uphill through the Centre back to the car park.

Walk Number 3

Carrock Fell

by Susan Beale

Purpose	To examine the rocks of the eastern end of Carrock Fell and depositional features nearby.

Practical Details

Starting Point	Park beside the fell road opposite Stone End Farm. (NY 354 338).
Walk Description	Severe: Approx. 5km, 420m steep climb to summit, followed by rough hill walking and steep descent.
Maps	1:25 000 OL5 The English Lakes North eastern area.
Public Transport	Occasional bus service from Keswick Bus Station to Caldbeck.
Public Toilets	None – nearest at Caldbeck (9kms).
Refreshments	Pub at Mungrisdale; Pub & café at Hesket Newmarket.

NOTE: This walk should only be undertaken in dry weather with very good visibility. It involves steep climbs and uses indistinct paths on exposed fell tops. It could be hazardous in poor conditions.

GEOLOGICAL SETTING

Carrock Fell consists of a variety of **igneous** rocks **intruded** at a depth of several kilometres into the thick sediments of the Skiddaw Group about 450**Ma**. Carrock Fell is part of the base of what was a high mountain. The rocks forming the top of the mountain have been eroded away over millions of years to expose the igneous rocks that now form Carrock Fell. It is bounded by Skiddaw Group rocks to the south and west. To the east and north are Eycott volcanic rocks, mostly covered by glacial sediment.

EXCURSION DESCRIPTION

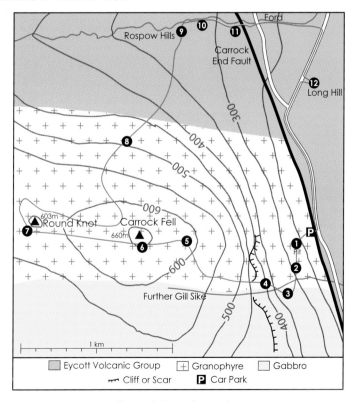

Figure 1. Excursion route.

Locality 1 (NY 353 336) is the small quarry at the foot of the fells where angular blocks of varied sizes have fallen from the cliffs. The blocks consist of two different sorts of igneous rocks - light coloured **granophyre** and dark **gabbro**. Their angularity and varied size suggest these rocks have not travelled far.

From Locality 1 walk to the foot of the cliff and pick up the path which tracks diagonally steeply uphill to cross a scree slope. Pause on the scree, *Locality 2* (NY 351 335). The valley below is covered by poorly drained glacial **till** producing boggy, rough ground. This valley was a major route for ice moving from the central fells to the Solway Firth during the Devensian glaciation (c. 50 000**BP**). The hills to the southeast, have an irregular stepped topography. They are composed of Eycott **Lavas**, the earliest of the huge volume of Ordovician lava flows, (the Borrowdale Volcanics), which make up the central Lakeland fells. Beyond the Eycott Lavas, the smoother hills of Carboniferous Limestone form the eastern skyline.

Having enjoyed the view, examine the scree slope. It consists of blocks of granophyre, a coarse grained, pinkish rock weathering to pale grey. Individual crystals, of **quartz** and **feldspar** (best seen on a fresh face) interlock, giving a graphic texture. Granophyre forms the cliffs of Scurth that tower immediately above. Continue to Further Gill Syke, then leave the path to cross the gill to the cliffs of dark rocks to the south, *Locality 3* (NY 351 333). This is gabbro, another igneous rock with large black and white crystals giving a rough texture, and a speckled appearance on fresh surfaces. The light minerals are feldspars, the dark ones **amphiboles**, rich in iron and magnesium. The purplish red colour of the weathered surfaces is due to the oxidation of iron from the amphiboles. Both the granophyre and the gabbro formed from **magma** which cooled slowly (deep in the earth) allowing time for the large crystals to grow.

Rejoin the grassy path. Just above the loose stones climb to 5m above the juniper bush on the right. Take a faint sheep trod contouring north for 25m to **Locality 4** (NY 350 334), below the higher of two pine trees. We are back on granophyre but, at Locality 4, it is cut by a dark, fine-grained **andesitic dyke** marked by several round sample holes. The small size of the crystals in this younger dyke indicate it was formed from magma which cooled fairly quickly, perhaps because the cold host rock chilled the small volume quickly or because the intrusion occurred at shallow depth. Both reasons may be valid.

Return to the path and climb steeply up a narrow gully to emerge onto a heather covered plateau. Southwards the gabbros, seen at Locality 3, form a line of cliffs. Follow the track west, slightly uphill, to a small sheepfold. Continue upwards across a granophyre boulder scree to Pike (NY 345 337), **Locality 5**. From this elevated position look down northwards to a conspicuous long, green, grass-covered ridge, surrounded by rough ground, just northeast of the fork in the road. This is the esker at Locality 12. Continue west towards the summit of Carrock Fell. Just to the right of the footpath at (NY 34212 33654) is a 1m diameter boulder of granophyre which has been intruded by a fine grained light coloured magma – evidence for continued movement of magma after the granophyre had crystallised. The summit plateau is ringed by a ramp of blocks of granophyre marking the boundary of an Iron Age Romano-British hill fort.

Locality 6 is Carrock Fell summit (NY 342 336), formed of granophyre with pronounced **joint** planes dipping southwards. Among the loose boulders of granophyre are a few of dark gabbro. Gabbro outcrops lower down. The boulders were brought to the summit by the upward movement of an ice sheet.

From the summit, proceed west to **Locality 7,** the low outcrops of microgabbro, (a fine grained gabbro) which form Round Knott, 603m (NY 334 337). This microgabbro is composed of layers of darker

augite and paler **plagioclase** minerals, best seen on the west faces of the outcrop 25m south of Round Knott summit. It is thought that the microgabbro formed from a magma that crystallised slowly at depth. As the crystals formed they sank to form layers at the bottom of the magma chamber. Augite minerals are rich in iron and magnesium so their early precipitation depleted the magma of these elements. The magma then precipitated plagioclase minerals (rich in aluminium and calcium) until the chemical balance was restored and augite could again be precipitated. Thus alternating layers of minerals accumulated and are now recognised in the field by their different colours. Much later, when the magma had cooled further, increased pressure caused the mass of almost solid rock to be intruded into the overlying Skiddaw Group sediments. Either in the magma chamber or during the intrusion, the layers were distorted to form the disturbed and convoluted layers visible at Round Knott. See Figure 2.

Figure 2. Distorted layering in microgabbro on Round Knott
(note pencil for scale) (Photo S. Beale)

Leave Round Knott by the track running northwest to look at more similar outcrops, until an east-west path is met. Here turn eastwards back towards the summit of Carrock Fell.

At the foot of the ramparts follow a narrow sunken path northwards for 100m. Then bear northwest (310°) picking up a track which becomes increasingly clear as it descends to **Locality 8,** a very boggy patch on the path. Here excellent views to the northwest show the mineral workings of Driggith Mine. These were originally worked for lead but latterly – until 1966 – for **barytes**.

Continue downhill to the valley floor, mantled with thick glacial till. Cross gently sloping ground towards two small rounded hills, the Rospow Hills, **Locality 9** (NY 345 350). Follow the small path round the western hill to reach Carrock Beck. Before reaching the ford look back at a small scar on the hill revealing that it is composed of unconsolidated sediments. These sediments may have accumulated in a large pool on the surface of the melting ice sheet. When the ice sheet melted completely (about 10,000 BP) the accumulated sediments were deposited to form these rounded hills.

At the ford turn downstream (no path). Here the beck is cutting a valley into the unconsolidated glacial sediment. 50m downstream at **Locality 10** (NY 344 350), a scar on the south side reveals the poorly sorted character of a typical glacial till – large and small boulders set randomly in fine grained matrix.

Continue downstream to a small gorge, **Locality 11** (NY 347 351). Between gorse bushes you may be able to see the dark grey, fine-grained bedrock. It is an andesite, part of the Eycott Volcanic Formation and was formed from runny lava which erupted, perhaps from a fissure, to cool very quickly. The andesite resists erosion better than the unconsolidated glacial till, so the beck is cutting a gorge here. Continue downstream, cross the road and go east across the common to reach a second road. Follow this road southwards for about 100m then bear east across the moor to Long Hill, a 4m high ridge, parallel to and 70m east of the road. This is **Locality 12** (NY 354 346), the esker viewed from Locality 4. The quarry in the north end of the hill exposes well-sorted layers of pebbles and cobbles of a wide range of rock types. See Figure 3.

Figure 3. The Quarry in Long Hill .
The arrow indicates the alignment of pebbles in the esker.
(Photo S. Beale)

The rounded pebbles contrast with the angular blocks seen in Locality 1 and indicate that the pebbles have been transported some distance by water. Their varied composition reflects sources to the south and west. The larger cobbles could only be moved by water with a velocity of 60cm/sec, much higher than the present day streams nearby. These cobbles were probably carried by subglacial streams flowing under pressure within an ice sheet. Eskers are characteristic of areas of stagnant ice, and are among the last features to be formed as an ice sheet melts. From the southern end of the hill rejoin the road and walk south to the start.

Walk Number 4

Glenridding Landforms and Landscapes

by Richard Clark

Purpose	To examine the character of a pre-glacial landscape and the effects of subsequent glaciations.

Practical Details

Starting Point	LDNP car park in the centre of Glenridding (NY 386 169).
Walk Description	Approx. 7.5km, 550m ascent to ridge Steep start. Mainly good paths: fell walking. Inappropriate in low cloud.
Maps	1:25 000 Explorer OL 5 The English Lakes Northeastern Area. 1:50 000 Landranger Sheet 90, Penrith, Keswick and Ambleside.
Public Tranport	Bus from Penrith, summer services link Glenridding with Keswick and Bowness.
Public Toilets	In LDNP carpark.
Refreshments	Cafes and licensed premises in Glenridding village.

GEOLOGICAL SETTING

The study area includes Glenridding and Grisedale, glaciated troughs from the Helvellyn watershed to Ullswater. The route largely follows the intervening ridge. The local rocks, of the Upper Ordovician Borrowdale Volcanic Group, are varied, **tuffs** (hardened volcanic ash) being prominent. The area is within the Troutbeck Zone: north-south **faults** have influenced the local valley pattern and alignment of small features, gullies and cross-spur cols. There were small quarries, mostly for slate, and two lead mines, small at Eagle Crag, Grisedale (closed 1877) and very large at Greenside, Glenridding (NY 365 174), which worked from the seventeenth century until 1962.

Diversity of paths gives a wide choice of routes, longer, harder, to shorter, easier and with variety of perspectives on topics. The excursion described here could be extended or varied. Figure 1 shows the excursion route while Figure 2 places mentioned in the text.

EXCURSION DESCRIPTION

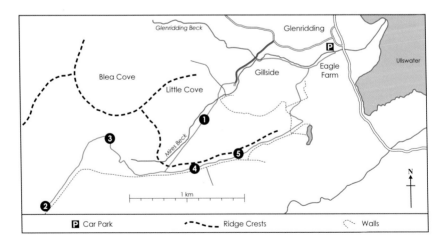

Figure 1. Excursion Route.

On leaving the car park turn and look west to the facing hillside, the end of Birkhouse Moor.   Little Cove is on the left, Blea Cove, facing northeast, on the right.   Now cross the A 592 road bridge, turn right (west) between beck and shops, past village hall and Eagle Farm. At fork, (signpost) keep right near beck (left is return route). At the road turn left (southwest) uphill and pass Gillside Farm.   Little Cove and Blea Cove are now near.   They resemble **corries** (**cirques**) but their bases are at 250m OD: rather low for local corries. Also, they do not have the flatter floors characteristic of 'true' corries. How might 'non-corrie corrie-like' shapes be made? Continue onto the fellside, and take the main uphill path (signposted Helvellyn), then at the final fell wall (gate and ladder stile) turn left crossing to the south side of Mires Beck after 100m into Little Cove.

Locality 1 (NY 375 165) is Little Cove.   Pause on the climb for views and to note nearby landforms. Glenridding Dodd (NY 383 176) shows landforms due to ice-erosion and carries some later scree. The knick (Rake) just to its west is fault-guided. Ullswater fills the impressive ice-eroded trough between Glenridding Dodd and Place Fell (NY 406 169). See photograph, Figure 3. Islands in Ullswater and rock outcrops forming small hills through the alluvium at Patterdale suggest the existence of rock bars in the trough floor separating more deeply eroded basins. The distant Pennine scarp was, other than its highest parts, covered by ice from the Lake District and Scotland in the fullness of the last glaciation. Imagine the thickness of the ice sheet over all the local hills when ice could be sent from here across the Pennines and as far as the North Sea. Note also rather flat high parts in the landscape, like the north end of Place Fell where rocks **dipping** south have been bevelled. The steep west side of Place Fell shows rougher (ice-plucked) and smoother (ice-abraded) parts formed by ice moving north down the Ullswater valley. Mires Beck flows in a cut through a debris tongue aligned down Little Cove. There are good examples of boulder-flow (saturated mixes of boulders and fine sediment) in the gully. The present stream attains neither power nor depth to build the deposits but torrents, possibly beneath a glacier, might have moved such a mixture.

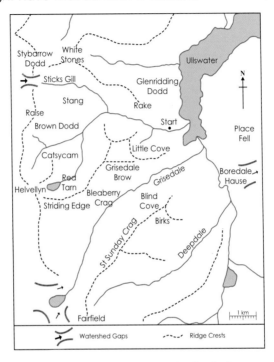

Figure 2. Places mentioned in the text.

Above the steep climb out of Little Cove the path approaches a long east-west wall. Near a cairn, pick out a less-used path which leads east alongside the wall (about NY 371 160). This is the return route (described below: Locality 2) and a suitable turning point to make a short excursion. The westward path rises near the wall but soon turns away to the north on a well-built track (not marked on OS maps) to reach the 700m ridge at (NY 365 163). Follow the path along the crest back to and then along the wall. Ahead, the crest narrows. Here is a transition. To the east, valley widening, especially of Grisedale, did not consume all the broad ridge top. To the west ice erosion and slope failure reduced the ridge top to a narrow **arête** – Striding Edge.

West   Glenridding Dodd   Pennines   Place Fell   East

Figure 3. View from near Little Cove looking northeast.
(Photo by E. Clark)

From **Locality 2** (NY 363 150), the most distant point of the excursion, the collapsed south ridge of the Bleaberry Crag (NY 358 152) ridge can be seen. Some of the slipped parts are very clear. Take in the character of the landscape in the fine, extensive views to east and southeast.

Look north and west too. Red Tarn is in a perched (hanging) valley over 700m. North of Glenridding trough the lip of the perched Sticks Gill valley and the fall of the beck near Lucy's Tongue to Greenside are obvious. Between Raise (NY 343 174) and the trough-side the bench (Brown Dodd, NY 352 172 and Stang, NY 354 176) may be part of an older landscape, least changed by glaciation. Beyond, fairly gentle ridge profiles (Stybarrow Dodd, White Stones) may tell the same story. Consider such a landscape at the onset of glaciation. Ice from high snowfields would move slowly and spread more widely than would streams of water. Most ice would follow existing valleys and converge in the largest. In general ice erodes more effectively the greater its thickness. Valleys with the thickest ice were the most eroded while those with thinnest ice were least eroded. This explains differences in valley sizes. The main valleys could be converted into deep troughs such as Glenridding and Grisedale

The precipitous north face of Catstye Cam (NY 348 158) demands notice: it looks as if it was chopped through and, in a sense, it has been. The Glenridding trough starts with two valleyhead corries, Keppel Cove and Brown Cove. The steep ridge-end of Catstye Cam 'got in the way' of the Glenridding glacier, which probably cut it back over several glaciations. It makes a short spectacular ridge-end length of trough wall. Most of the trough deepening was further down valley. Blea Cove might have been shaped, at different times, by ice moving down Glenridding or from the southwest. There may also have been rockfalls from their steepened sides. Little Cove, on the other hand, probably owes most to ice that moved down its length. Return along the same path.

Locality 3 is the small cove above Little Cove. It is well seen during descent. Ice from the west crossed it, but at some stages in glaciations it could have generated its own ice. Note the joints dipping south roughly parallel to the wall: they may well have promoted instability on the north side of Grisedale. Turn onto the wallside return path.

Locality 4 (NY 373 160) is the highest point of the path with good views up Grisedale. See photograph, Figure 4. In a hollow (c. NY372 160, 470m) a stone stile allows a short diversion to see the north side, with back slopes (slipped slices of hillside?) round NY 371 157, on Grisedale Brow (NY 365 155) and Bleaberry Crag.

There are three corries (Cock Cove, Ruthwaite Cove and Nethermost Cove) near the head of Grisedale and all on its west side. Grisedale is a trough right from its watershed, its steep upper stream course giving way to a long, much more gentle, lower one (see figure 4), unlike Glenridding.   Valley-head gaps across the crest probably fed in blown snow from the Grasmere area so supplementing the erosive power of successive glaciers in Grisedale.   Sticks Pass at the head of Sticks Gill is probably too high to have let as much ice across the ridge though blown snow probably nourished ice accumulation there. The southern valley side towards Fairfield (NY 359 117) has many features of slope failure and the steep slope beneath St Sunday Crag for about 1.5km southwest from Blind Cove (NY 374 143) is similar. These hillsides are crossed by major faults: small tremors may have been enough to unsettle these steepened valley sides. Walk 400m to a view point.

Figure 4. Upper Grisedale looking southwest from location 4.
Note the trough form extends down from the Watershed Gap.
(sf - slope failure)   (Photo by E. Clark)

Locality 5 (NY 377 161). Here is a better view of lower Grisedale. Birks (NY 382 145), across Grisedale, has a very level crest. Its slope into Grisedale is much moulded by ice (some from Deepdale), down to the cliff. Above this cliff are small hillside scars perhaps indicating tension associated with ice steepening of the lower valley side. The broader views here are less fine than from higher points but still give a good impression of the high, more subdued, older landscape. Visualise the landscape when, long before the glaciations, the main valley floors were 200 or more metres above their present levels. Later uplift of the land gave potential for deepening of valleys. Then came the glaciers with the power to exploit that potential. Ice also crossed east from Ullswater into Martindale over the saddle south of Place Fell.

There are good examples near the ridge-top path of ice-abraded and ice-plucked sides of outcrops. Follow the wall heading for the west end of a conifer plantation (NY 382 163), go along its north side, turn left to a more-used path down to Glenridding village.

Walk Number 5

Cross Fell and the Pennine Escarpment

by John Rodgers

Purpose	To observe the landscape features and rocks of the Pennine Escarpment and southern end of the Cross Fell Inlier.

Practical Details

Starting Point	Car Park in centre of Dufton Village – (NY 689 250).
Walk Description	The full walk is 15 km with approximately 400 metres of ascent but short cuts are possible. It is inadvisable (and potentially dangerous) in poor visibility or bad weather.
Maps	1:50 000 Landranger Sheet 91 (Appleby-in-Westmorland area). 1:25 000 Explorer OL19 (Howgill Fells and Upper Eden Valley).
Public Transport	There is no regular service to Dufton.
Public Toilet	At car park.
Refreshments	Public House in Dufton Village. NB the Post Office/shop in Dufton Village has now closed.

GEOLOGICAL SETTING

This excursion is a traverse from the low-lying Eden Valley up onto the Pennine escarpment. Permian and Triassic age sediments occupy the lower ground, mainly overlain by glacial **till**. The upper part of the Pennine slope consists of interbedded limestones, **shales** and sandstones into which the Whin **Sill** was emplaced. Between these two areas, forming the lower part of the scarp slope is the geological feature known as the Cross Fell **Inlier**. This strip of land, stretching 25 km. from Melmerby in the north to beyond Hilton in the south, is rarely more than 2km. wide. It forms a distinctive landscape of small hills and steep-sided valleys. The most striking features are the conical "pikes" of Knock, Dufton and Murton. The rocks of the inlier are Lower **Palaeozoic** and extend below the younger Carboniferous of the Pennines. These older formations, similar to those of the Lake District, have been exposed by earth movements along the Pennine **fault** zone, which resulted in massive uplift of the Pennine block relative to the Eden Valley. These relationships between the main elements of the area are shown in Figure 1.

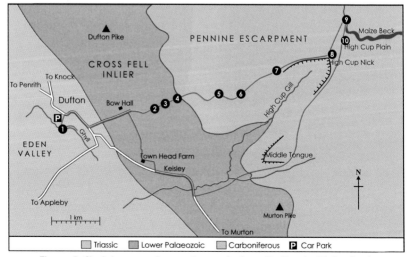

Figure 1. Sketch map of excursion route from Dufton to Maize Beck.

EXCURSION

Locality 1 (NY 691 248) Dufton Ghyll Wood. Take the path next to the car park and descend into the wooded valley where a small gorge has been eroded through the red Triassic sandstone, visible in the old quarry faces over the footbridge and upstream. **Cross-bedding** indicates these were water-laid sediments. Return to the car park and drive south to the edge of the village, then turn left at the bridge on to the Pennine Way. Park on the verge past Bow Hall (c.1.5km from the Dufton car park), before the gate across the road. Roughly 0.5km. up the road from the bridge you cross a major fault line and pass from the Triassic into the Cross Fell Inlier rocks, buried beneath a cover of glacial deposits.

Locality 2 (NY 711 250) is the small barn to the left of the Pennine Way Path (PWP). From the end of the surfaced road follow the track for about 700m to a small barn on the left. Bedrock is not exposed but the underlying material consists of a variety of pale-coloured volcanic rocks. Some stones in the walls (do not remove any) or loose pieces in the track show dark parallel streaks. These are **ash-flow tuffs** equivalent to the Borrowdale Volcanic Group rocks of the Lake District and are probably from a small, disused quarry in a field on the left further up the track (NY 713 252). The quarry is on private land but can be seen from the gate. The walls also include numerous blocks of white vein **quartz.**
To the south from here observe a dry valley between two hills of resistant volcanic rocks. Such valleys are common in this region and represent glacial drainage channels, eroded or deepened by meltwater during deglaciation. Note also evidence of a landslip on the lower slopes of Gregory, the hill on the left (east) side of the valley.

Locality 3 (PWP track up to NY 715 252). Dark grey fine-grained rocks appear quite abruptly in small outcrops in the track. These are mainly **siltstones** of the Ordovician Murton Formation, and are interpreted as deep-sea sediments, equivalent to the Skiddaw Group of the Lake District, thus representing the oldest rocks in the region. In one outcrop about 100m from the gate there are highly inclined partings either **bedding** or **cleavage** planes?, an indication of strong folding.

Another meltwater channel can be seen to the south and a slight change in slope gradient on the western (right) side probably marks the boundary between the less resistant sediments and the harder volcanic rocks.

Locality 4 (PWP track from NY 715 252 to NY 723 250). The change from the older rocks of the inlier to the overlying and **unconformable** Carboniferous beds occurs roughly halfway between the two gateways on this section of the path. Dark grey fragments in the track gradually give way to small outcrops of greenish sandstone with the occasional thin band of **conglomerate.** These are the Basement Beds but the **unconformity** itself is not exposed.
From here there is a good view of the inlier landforms to the north with the harder volcanic rocks of Dufton Pike and Knock Pike standing out as isolated resistant hills.

Locality 5 (NY 723 250) is through the gate above the walled enclosure. It is in an area of abundant outcrops of the pale grey Melberby Limestone. This is the first of a series of limestones which form prominent and usually horizontal bands (known as scars) in the Pennine escarpment. Above the path, to the left is an old limekiln below which the small screes may be searched. Fossil corals and **brachiopods** have been found here. From a path above the limekiln, look southeast across to Murton Pike. Compressional earth-movements have forced older rocks of the inlier (Murton Formation) up and over the Carboniferous, producing a clear dislocation in the limestone scar which abruptly ends at the plane of the Murton Pike Fault.

Figure 2. View of Murton Pike and approximate position of the faulted junction between the Murton Formation and the Carboniferous Limestone.
(Photo J. Rogers)

This same limestone forms the platform of Middle Tongue above High Cup Gill. Note how the prominent ridge at the lower end of the valley has been cut into by the river. This ridge is an extensive mound of **fluvio glacial** deposit, formed as high-energy meltwater dropped material at the margin of a glacier. Continue on the PNP for a few hundred metres.

Locality 6 (NY 727 253) is where the PWP crosses through an extensive area of large angular blocks of pale quartz sandstones with abundant 'rusty' spots. Cross-bedding in some of the blocks and the linear form of the mapped outcrop (a similar patch can be seen across the valley on Middle Tongue) suggests this was a channel sand deposit. Follow the path for c.1.5km noting the

following features:
- The magnificent view into the valley of High Cup Gill.
- A definite spring line on the opposite hillside below Middle Tongue which probably marks the unconformable junction between the Carboniferous and the older rocks below.
- Evidence of landslips on the opposite valley side.
- The prominent line of vertical crags formed by the Whin Sill.

Eventually the path levels off and a stone slab is reached with an arrow indicating left. As a more interesting option follow the old path to the right across 'pavements' of strongly jointed dark grey limestone.

Locality 7 (NY 736 259) is where Strands Beck crosses the path. Above the deeply weathered limestone is a sequence of crumbly black shales containing numerous hard nodules of ironstone up to several cm long.   Across the valley the vertical columns of the Whin Sill can be clearly seen. These were formed by the development of **joints** (fractures) as the hot sheet of magma solidified, cooled and contracted. Much of the valley side opposite is landslip material but erosional gulleys in places have exposed the horizontal **sedimentary** beds.

Locality 8 (NY 745 262) High Cup Nick and the Whin Sill. See Figure 3. Rejoin the main path and pass through an area of large blocks of fallen sandstone from the ridge above. Numerous large shake holes (where the solution of the limestone below has caused the collapse of overlying beds) occur in the flatter ground beyond. Follow the edge round to the right to arrive at High Cup Nick from where there is an impressive view of the glacial trough shape of the main valley. The outcrops here are of a hard, black fine-grained rock with pale metallic spots of **pyrite**. This is the **basaltic** top surface of the Whin Sill, the margin that rapidly cooled against the overlying limestone. It is not safe to get close to the upper contact zone but descend the path by the stream to a section through the sill. Note how the grain size increases in the main part of the **intrusion** where cooling was slower so the rock becomes a dark grey-green **dolerite**. The lower contact can be seen by carefully crossing the fallen block field to the left of the path to a small platform. Look for a chilled margin of black, almost glassy basalt above a thin zone of pale granular rock **(metaquartzite)** formed by the **thermal metamorphism** of the underlying fine sandstone. Now return to High Cup Nick and proceed northwesterly across High Cup Plain to rejoin the PWP. (Avoid the very boggy direct route). Cross through an area of highly weathered limestone pavement with widely spaced **clints.**

Locality 9 (NY 749 270) is a footbridge over a gorge in Maize Beck. After c.1km there is a footbridge across a small gorge. The bedrock below is a black limestone, with a surface polished and dimpled by water action. Sections through brachiopods and corals are visible in a few places. The narrow channel opens out downstream where an underlying bed of black shale has been eroded out resulting in the collapse of large blocks of limestone into the valley.

Locality 10 (NY 748 265) is a **Barytes** vein. Heading south back across High Cup Plain brings you to a line of old workings, probably an exploration for lead. Small pieces of dense white barytes can be found in the spoil heaps. Continue along the route that runs just above the Whin Sill on the southeast side of the valley. This gives excellent views and an opportunity to examine features referred to on the walk up. The path is not shown on older maps but is now way-marked. After about 3 km join a farm track which descends southwest to Harbour Flatt. Keeping the farm to your left continue on the track for a further 300m to join the minor road that leads back to Dufton. There is a short cut from Keisley to vehicles parked at Bow Hall and this would enable a stop at Town Head Farm where a winery and small vineyard are being established.

Refreshments and information about the local geology are also available here.
(Details from www.highcupwines.co.uk)

Figure 3. View of High Cup Nick and the Whin Sill from the southeast.

Walk Number 6

Vale of Eden

by Gordon Taylor

Purpose	To look at rocks of Permian and Triassic Age, formed about 250 million years ago, in the Upper Eden Valley.

Practical Details

Starting Point	Public path near Black Bull Inn at Nateby (NY 772 065).
Walk Description	A series of walks in a south to north traverse along the upper Eden Valley of easy to moderate difficulty.
Maps	1:25 000 OL19 Howgill Fells & Upper Eden Valley 1:50 000 Landranger Sheet 91 Appleby-in-Westmorland area 1:50 000 British Geological Survey Sheets 24, 30, 31 & 40.
Public Transport	Bus service Kirkby Stephen to Temple Sowerby.
Public Toilets	Kirkby Stephen, Appleby and Dufton.
Refreshments	Nateby, Kirkby Stephen, Appleby, Dufton and Temple Sowerby.

GEOLOGICAL SETTING

Today the River Eden meanders through lush fields and woods bulwarked by the rugged hills of the Lake District to the west and the Pennine range to the east and south. Ovoid **drumlins**, consisting of relatively thick deposits from ice sheets, cover the bedrock and form a gently rolling landscape. However, about 250 million years ago the scenery and environment was quite different! Picture if you will a scene like the Middle East and North Africa today. These areas are characterised by an intense hot and arid climate, windswept and polished rock pavements, and sand dunes. They contain shallow lakes that periodically dry up. From time to time fierce thunderstorms produce flash floods that carve through the landscape forming wadis, sweeping all before them and depositing sediments in an irregular fan-shape. This was Britain around 250**Ma**. (see Figure 4). Studies of the magnetic declination from iron-rich particles in the rocks suggests that from 267 to 249 Ma the Vale of Eden was situated between 15°N and 25°N – roughly where the Middle East and North Africa are today. The rocks are difficult to date because they have very few fossils and the stratigraphy is complicated. The sequence straddles the boundary between the Permian and Triassic Periods (Figure 1). In the Eden valley the boundary between the two Periods is tentatively placed at about 35m above the Belah **Dolomite** (Figure 1) but the junction in Britain is not clearly defined.

The Pennine **Fault** system forms the eastern boundary of a **half-graben** for the Vale of Eden. There is evidence of an earlier scarp face at this eastern boundary before Middle Permian times, long before the present Pennine scarp was formed (Figure 4). The Triassic Sherwood Sandstone Group of sediments **overlap** the underlying older rocks. The half-graben was probably initiated when the tectonic plates began to move apart to open the sea that eventually became the Atlantic Ocean.

EXCURSION DESCRIPTION

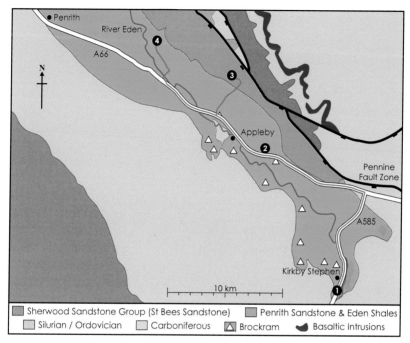

Figure 1. *Excursion route showing different rock types.*

The following localities (Figure 1) are starting points for several relatively short, often circular walks as indicated below.

Locality 1 - Nateby (NY 772 068)   At Nateby take the public path about 200m north of the Black Bull (NY 774 069) and walk west towards the River Eden.   Permission to go off the path must be obtained from Wharton Hall. The **unconformity** below the Permian rocks may be seen along the lower slopes of the nearby fells where Carboniferous limestones and sandstones underlie the Permian. By retracing your steps, exposures that afford a three-dimensional views of lens shaped bodies of **Brockram** may be viewed, see Figure 2. The Brockram was formed from **alluvial fan** deposits.   It consists of angular pebbles, mostly of Carboniferous limestone, supported by a matrix of sand-size particles.

Figure 2. Brockram composed of angular pebbles of Carboniferous limestone.
(Photo M.Dodd)

Here the fans appear to have been derived from sediments to the west with some evidence of upward fining of the sequence. This may be due to the erosion of the overall topography, which would have reduced the energy of streams and thus the size of the particles carried. Further to the east (NY 775 068) in a vertical face of a disused quarry, there are tabular layers of pebbly sandstones separated by **shales** that were probably also deposited by rivers. These have been correlated with the Lower Triassic rocks in Stenkrith Park.

Proceed towards Kirkby Stephen where the second of ten Eden Benchmark sculptures that celebrate the new Millennium from the source to the mouth of the River Eden may be seen in Stenkrith Park (NY 773 076). Here there is a spectacular gorge through the

Brockram where the deposit is younger than at Nateby, and is part of the Upper Permian (Figure 1). Walk along the dismantled railway track observing the red sandstones similar to those at the last exposure at Nateby. These occur directly on the Brockram, indicating that the Lower Triassic rocks infilled hollows of the older irregular topography. After 2km the path leads to the quarry entrance at Hartley (NY 785 085) where Carboniferous rocks are being excavated. The restored viaducts give fine views of the Pennine fells and gills.

At Belah Bridge (NY 793 121) about 3.5km north of Kirkby Stephen towards Brough, take a path along the north bank of the River Belah to an exposure that is crucial in deciphering the geological history in the Vale of Eden. About 1km to the east there is a 5m exposure of the Belah Dolomite and dolomitic shales in a small bluff south of the river (NY 802 122). Fossils of marine animals from this exposure indicate that it represents an incursion by the supersaline Zechstein Sea in Upper Permian times (see Figure 4). Near the main road in the cliffs at Belah Scar (NY 794 120), there is a fine exposure of variegated sandstones with basal scours filled with gravel. These sandstones fine upward to thin mudstones belonging to the Middle Permian that also outcrop in these cliffs (NY 794 120). This exposure shows sediments deposited by short-lived rivers and illustrates the complex sedimentary relationships within both The Permian rocks.

Locality 2 - George Gill bluffs (NY 718 189). From Coupland walk towards Appleby Golf Course. Take the footpath (starting at NY 715 193) to the west-southwest along George Gill to the bluffs.

Figure 3. Dune bedded sandstone at George Gill bluffs.
(Photo M. Dodd)

Excellent large scale (indicating they are wind-borne), dune-bedded red sandstones of the (Penrith Sandstone) may be observed on the south side of the gill. The westerly dips of the **foreset beds** indicate that they were formed by winds blowing from the east. Regular cracks in the rocks that are picked out by thin quartz **veins** can be seen on the north side, see Figure 3. These fractures were all formed at roughly the same time and the pattern suggests they were the result of horizontal extension of the rocks resulting in **normal faults**. This can be confirmed by minor amounts of relative movement along some fractures. Do these minor fractures mirror larger structures operating in Permian times?

The next locality may be reached through Appleby, where more exposures of the dune-bedded sandstones may be observed along the roadside. Alternatively take an easy walk of 6km through Brackenber and Murton following the Pennine Fault Zone scarp with the distant exposure of the Whin **Sill** at the spectacular High Cup Nick.   At Brackenber take the northerly footpath to an exposure of the Hilton Plant Beds near a footbridge over Hilton Beck (NY 721 206). This horizon of transported plant debris represents sheet flood deposits along the margin of a temporary intermontane **playa** lake and was deposited at roughly the same time as the 'A' **Gypsum** Bed of the Upper Permian (Figure 1).

Locality 3 Redbanks Quarry, Dufton (NY 693 247). Taking the track to the east of the car park (NY 690 240) walk down to a small wooden bridge and enter a wooded abandoned quarry where an excellent vertical section along the **strike** of the Lower Triassic (Sherwood Sandstone Group) is exposed. The foxy-brown sandstones were deposited by rivers and show small scale **cross-bedding** with a variety of current directions, mainly to the west. These beds reflect fluvial conditions contrasting with the sheet flood environment of the Hilton Beds. The stone was used extensively for local buildings and quarrymen's graffiti can still be seen.

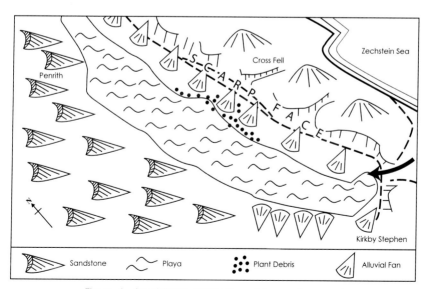

Figure 4. An oblique aerial view of the environment of the Vale of Eden during the Upper Permian.

Locality 4 - Newbiggin gypsum mine portal (NY 628 279). From Temple Sowerby (NY 616 271), take the footpath to Acorn Bank Cottages and turn right onto the minor road. After 300m turn right (southeast) on to a footpath to Newbiggin gypsum mine passing the restored Houtsay Quarry that was worked during the 1980s for gypsum. The remains of the Acorn Bank gypsum mine are adjacent to the road in the woods. They were probably the first working of gypsum in the Vale. The Acorn Bank watermill provided power for the underground endless rope haulage system. The mine which worked both the 'B' and 'C' Beds, was connected to the Kirkby Thore Works via an aerial ropeway that transported the mined gypsum. The 'B' and 'C' Beds of the Upper Permian are exposed, on the southeast side of the portal of Newbiggin Mine. These are about 30m below the Belah Dolomite (Figure 1). The 'B' Bed is 5-6m thick, resting on dark shales, the gypsum being pinkish-grey with fine-grained texture often with darker selenite (a type of gypsum) crystals. The 'C' Bed is 1m thick and displays a laminated structure formed by algae. The **evaporites** of the Group are mainly gypsum and anhydrite (anhydrous calcium sulphate) but include a 7m thick halite (sodium chloride – common salt) layer near the top of the 'A' Bed. These were formed as a sabkha (salt flat) deposit adjacent to a series of playa lakes. Permission to visit the locality must be obtained from the operators (British Gypsum).

Much of the Permian and Triassic geology of the Vale still remains unsolved. There is much the amateur geologist could contribute. *Acknowledgement* Noel Worley, of British Gypsum (British Plaster Board), provided stimulating discussions and encouragement.

Walk Number 7

Great Asby Limestone

by Simon Webb

Purpose	To experience spectacular limestone pavements.

Practical Details

Starting point	(NY 632 107) on east side of B6260 between Orton and Appleby, 800 metres north of the cattle grid and the junction with the lane to Crosby Ravensworth.
Walk Description	Moderate, approximately 7 kilometres (4.25 miles), over rough, stony ground.
Maps	1:25 000 OL19. Howgill Fells and Upper Eden Valley. 1:50 000 Landranger Map 91. Appleby in Westmorland area.
Public Transport	None.
Public Toilets	Orton or Appleby.
Refreshments	Many local tea-shops and pubs.

Important instruction - Please do not hammer.

GEOLOGICAL SETTING

The low limestone hills running between Shap and Kirkby Stephen north of the Howgill Fells form the edge of the Lake District dome. The limestone **dips** gently eastwards towards the Eden Valley. Fossil corals and marine shells found in these sedimentary rocks indicate that they were deposited in the bottom of a warm, shallow sea which covered north-west Europe 340 million years ago, during the Carboniferous Period. The rocks of Asby give their name to the Asbian, a term which is used internationally by geologists to describe any rocks of this age. On the northern and northeastern flanks of these hills are spectacular open limestone pavements. Sloping sheets of bare rock are criss-crossed with the cracks and blocks known respectively as **grikes** and **clints**. The pavements here are **folded** into a series of crests and troughs and their surface features pose questions about the age of the landscape, the nature of the ice age scouring and the role of soil and vegetation in shaping limestone landscapes.

Some 15 000**BP** Europe was in the grip of an ice age. Glaciers and ice sheets scoured and eroded the limestone which was subsequently covered in glacial **till**. Beneath this cover slightly acidic water has picked out the planes of weakness in the limestone producing the classic clint and grike patterning. Limestone pavements are rare in Britain, covering less than 3000 hectares in total. They have been removed or destroyed in many places.

EXCURSION DESCRIPTION

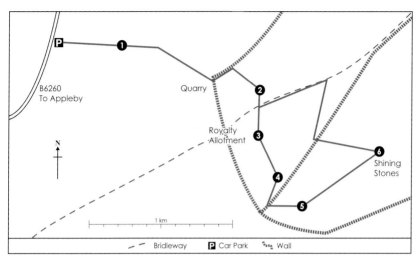

Figure 1. Excursion Map.

A well-marked track heads east from the road, crossing Gaythorn Plain. The limestone pavements here at **Locality 1** (NY 637 107) are extremely degraded, characterised by sheets of scree and rubble with few recognisable surface features. This area has had extensive stripping of pavement clints (blocks) to supply the demand for garden rockery stone until this ceased in 1996 when the planning permission was revoked. Removal of pavement destroys the geological features - a record of the ice age scouring and subsequent weathering. It also destroys the habitat for the ferns and flowers that rely on the niches provided by cracks and solution pockets. The pavements of Gaythorn Plain are no-longer of significant ecological or geological importance. Good examples of fossil corals (mostly *Syringopora*) can easily be found by the track. The matrix of limestone has, in many cases, been dissolved away to leave superb masses of colonial corals looking like organ pipes.

The track continues down past the small Pickering Quarry, about 1km beyond the car parking. The quarry supplies decorative and building stone but is also used as a storage area - all sorts of geological anomalies can be seen in the edge of the spoil heaps. Beyond the quarry the track turns sharp left and after 300m (climbing over a stile next to a field gate on the right) leads into the Great Asby Scar National Nature Reserve, owned and managed by Natural England.

The track rises gently some 300m to a view out over the stunning pavements of Great Asby Scar at **Locality 2** (NY 647 103). From here the scale and splendour of the Asby pavements is evident. Huge sheets of pavement dominate the view criss-crossed with deep grikes and fretted by surface patterning (Figure 2). Ferns and flowering herbs flourish in the grikes and spill out onto the tops of the clints.

Figure 2. Asby Limestone Pavement.
(Photo S. Webb)

Particularly obvious from here is the folded nature of the Asby pavements. The surfaces of the pavements lie along major **bedding planes**.   These formed planes of weakness that were picked out by the glacial scouring of the last ice age. Across the small valley to the southeast a band of pavements dip away then rise up towards the horizon. These limestone beds are gently folded into a **syncline** with the fold axis running northeast-southwest. The folds in the limestone formed in late Carboniferous times during the Hercynian Orogeny. This was a period of crustal upheaval and mountain building. Compression of the crust on a regional scale led to localised folding of the rocks- a feature picked out many millions of years later by the undulating pavements of Asby. This valley is structural and never had a stream running through it. Cross the valley (and bridleway) and pick your way up onto the biggest sheet of pavements. Grazing livestock have recently been removed from the nature reserve and this pavement is now characterised by dozens of small trees, which had previously been held in check by sheep. This area will probably never return to a wood – it is too exposed and the soils are too thin for extensive woodland to flourish.

This part of the nature reserve, known as Royalty Allotment, *Locality 3* (NY 647 099), has the most varied examples of pavement surface features. Crossing the main sheet of pavement, a series of large circular depressions some 1m deep and 2-3m wide are encountered. Consensus on how fast limestone is eroded suggests that these features are too big to have formed in the 15,000 years since the glacial scouring occurred. Current thinking is that these are the remains of much bigger (or deeper) pre-glacial features that have partially survived the scouring ice. Evidence of pre-glacial features, inherited from an older landscape are widespread across the Orton-Asby escarpment.

The surface features seen on the pavements at Locality 3 are outstanding. In particular there are sets of branching runnels (gutter-like channels) and also exceptionally long clints (4m plus) which are aligned along the **strike** and have runnelled downslope edges. The lower margins of this pavement sheet show solution features actively forming under a soil cover which is breaking up and receding, with good examples around (NY 650 103) where pavement and vegetation cover meet. The rounded runnels and clint edges on the limestone pavement are evidence of its formation under a soil cover and here we can examine its continuing development. It is thought that soil cover was formerly deeper and more extensive - it was probably man's impact (clearing forests and grazing livestock) that has resulted in soil being lost and the pavements emerging from beneath their cover. Copper mineralisation along joints has been exploited here and a few wide grikes have clearly been mined. Small samples of copper ore (**malachite**) can be found amongst the spoil piled on the pavement surface.

Leaving the sheet of pavements head southeast up the slope to *Locality 4* (NY 649 095) for a view out across a second syncline of folded pavement and of Castle Folds, a Romano British settlement on a prominent knoll. The pavements below on the steep limb of the fold have large features - wide grikes and deep channels. This again suggests a pre-glacial origin but it is possible they have formed through the action of cold melt waters at the end of the ice age; cold water can dissolve limestone more aggressively than warm. The obvious "mushrooms" of limestone in the small valley to the southeast have formed where the lower layer (or bed) of limestone is weaker and more fractured. Iron staining of the pavement here gives some areas a reddish tinge. Cross the wall by a ladder stile up to the right.

The view from the top of Castle Folds (**Locality 5** NY 650 094) is spectacular. This settlement was heavily fortified and ruined hut sites can be seen within the walls.

Walking northeast from Castle Folds the terrain drops away to a large expanse of pavement known as Shining Stones (**Locality 6** NY 655 098). When viewed from the Pennines on a wet day the smooth surface of this pavement gleams like a mirror. Clint size here is generally large with fewer solution runnels.

Figure 3. Shining Stones.
(Photo S. Webb)

Large smooth clints often form when a particular bed (or layer) of limestone is stronger with fewer joints. They can also be the result of patches of lime-rich glacial till which "shield" the limestone from erosion and inhibit grike or runnel development. A third possibility is that till or vegetation cover was eroded away at an earlier time before sub-soil erosion had a chance to produce more grikes and other surface features. Several large Shap **Granite erratics** on the northeast edge of this pavement confirm that the Lake District ice sheet must have forced itself over the Orton Fells down into the Eden Valley leaving distinctive pink granite markers of the ice flow.

Return to the starting point by re-tracing your steps. Alternatively from Shining Stones cross the wall at a ladder stile at (NY 651 099) to omit Castle Folds. A further possibility is to continue along the escarpment to Little Asby Scar (an area owned and managed by Friends of the Lake District) where the road between Sunbiggin Tarn and Little Asby can be joined.

Walk Number 8

Around Coniston and Tarn Hows

by John Gunner

Purpose	To examine the lower part of the Windermere Supergroup succession near the northern ends of Windermere lake and Coniston Water.

Practical Details

Starting Point	Ambleside for a car/minibus tour of 5 sites on minor roads.
Walk description	Each site up to 1km sometimes over rough/ boggy ground.
Maps	O.S. 1:50 000 Sheets 90 Penrith, Keswick and Ambleside and 97 Barrow in Furness and South Lakeland area. 1:25 000 OL7 The English Lakes, South-eastern area and OL6 The English Lakes, South-western area (for Timley Knott).
Facilities	At Ambleside, Hawkshead and Coniston.

GEOLOGICAL SETTING

Tarn Hows lies at the junction of the Upper Ordovician Borrowdale Volcanic Group and the overlying Ordovician and Silurian Windermere Supergroup. The latter are mainly **sedimentary** rocks. The volcanic rocks were uplifted and eroded before the deposition of the Windermere Supergroup. This break in deposition together with the **tectonic** activity produced an **unconformity**. The earliest sediments of the Windermere Supergroup are those of the Dent Group (formerly Coniston Limestone Formation) which are rich in the fossils of benthonic (bottom-dwelling) marine animals indicating that these sediments were deposited on the sea bed. Towards the end of this episode the sea deepened and overlying **mudstones** and **greywackes** were deposited. Windermere Supergroup rocks **dip** to the south or southeast and their outcrops run generally northeast to southwest. Many north-south trending **faults** cut across these outcrops. Large natural exposures are rare. Figure 1 locates Timley Knott and Figure 3 shows Localities 2-5. Figure 6 shows the rocks succession in the area.

EXCURSION DETAILS

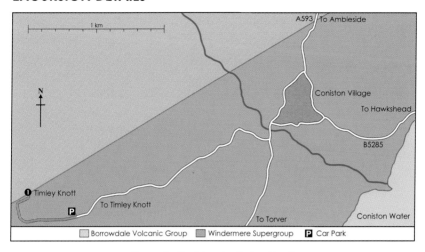

Figure 1. Coniston to Timley Knott.

Locality 1, Timley Knott (SD 283 971), is a craggy knoll near the base of the slope above the Walna Scar track, 2km west-southwest of Coniston village and 500 metres southeast of Bursting Stone quarry. To reach it from the petrol station in central Coniston proceed south to a cross-roads. Here take the road that heads uphill towards Walna Scar. After a right-hand and left-hand bend the road ascends very steeply. Continue uphill for 1km to a gate across the road. Park beyond and continue along the westward leading track for about 500m to the intersection (SD 272 969) of the quarry roadway and the Walna Scar track which makes a good viewpoint. From here steeply dipping beds of the Dent Group can be seen at the right and centre in contact with apparently unlayered massive volcanic rocks to the left (Figure 2). Approach via a steep grassy bank to the col at Point A (Figure 2). The rocks immediately to the southeast and northwest are dark grey **calcareous** mudstones and muddy limestones of the Applethwaite Formation, containing **brachiopods** and solitary **corals**. *Please do not hammer.* Weathering has formed pits and hollows up to 20cm in diameter where the rocks are most limy.

The silty beds are composed largely of volcanic fragments. The **laminations** and low-angle **cross-bedding** indicate these beds were water-lain.

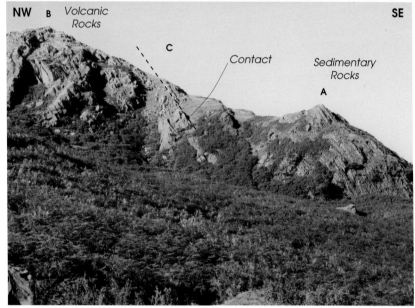

Figure 2. Timley Knott from the southwest.
(Photo M. Dodd)

Scramble up the rocky slope to Point B (Figure 2). Here the rocks are pale grey consisting of a fine matrix and angular fragments mostly 5-30mm across. The fragments have very fine-grained interiors and are isolated within the matrix. This suggests that both fragments and matrix are the result of a very violent eruption of material which cooled quickly as it fell on to the land, to become volcanic glass. Generally the finer and coarser layers grade into one another with poorly developed bedding dipping southeast, and are cut by a weak, steeply dipping cleavage. These rocks are the Lincombe Tarns Formation.

Descend carefully to Point C (Figure 2). Here the contact of the Lincombe Tarns Formation and the overlying Longsleddale Member (part of the Dent Group) is exposed on a sloping ledge facing southwest where both formations dip 30-40° to the southeast. The Longsleddale Formation is composed of very well rounded fragments up to 30cm across in a sand-grade matrix.   This is a **conglomerate** with the large fragments selectively weathered to form hollows The very well rounded fragments and lack of fine material in the matrix suggest lengthy exposure to a high energy environment: perhaps a river or a beach. The similarity of fragments and matrix to the underlying **tuffs** indicate that the tuffs provided the source material.

Lower down the slope creamy coloured rocks with sand size particles, derived from the tuffs, overlie the conglomerates.   The sand size suggests a less energetic environment, for example a river bar or a shore below a beach.

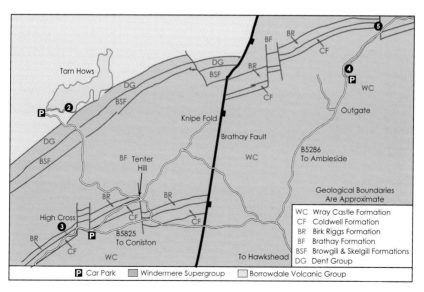

Figure 3. Map of localities around Tarn Hows.

Locality 2 (SD 330 997) is Tarn Hows which is National Trust property (Figure 3). **Please do not hammer rock exposures**. A dam at the southwest corner has created one lake from several small tarns. Park in the main western car park. Walk up the road to the eastern car park. Northeast of here sedimentary rocks of the Windermere Supergroup, which rest unconformably on the volcanic rocks, are tilted here to the southeast, forming an escarpment (Figures 4 and 5). Cliffs and benches mark the outcrops of more and less resistant beds. Go through the gate at the back of the car park and descend, skirting these outcrops, to a fence at the bottom of the slope. Beyond the track below this fence is a glaciated outcrop of grey-green tuff. It has a smooth up glacier surface and steeper down glacier slope,(**a roche moutonnée**). This represents the top of the enormous pile of Borrowdale Volcanic Group rocks that form the mountains to the west. Just above the fence are exposures of tough greenish quartz-veined rocks which weather brown and belong to the Longsleddale Formation These are conglomerates and sandstones, but they resemble the underlying tuff in colour and mineral content, because they were derived from volcanic debris. They were deposited on the eroded surface of the 'Borrowdale' volcano sometime after activity ceased about 450Ma. Scattered outcrops of sandstone extend up to the first bench above the basal three metres of these conglomerates and sandstones.

In the next cliff are limestones and interbedded mudstones. There is a pervasive **cleavage** dipping steeply and cutting across the bedding (Figures 4 and 5).

Figure 4 Windermere Supergroup rocks above Tarn Hows
showing bedding and cleavage.
(Photo M. Dodd)

The lowest exposed bed, a dark grey mudstone with cleavage striking east-northeast, crops out a few metres above a spring near the southern end of the bench. The limestones in this cliff are pale grey. Some are fossiliferous, some nodular, some pitted by the action of acid rainwater. Those with a higher clay content are cleaved.

The dark grey, cleaved and finely laminated beds southeast of the gully contain fossil fragments and are near the top of the Dent Group succession. Above these is a small exposure (by an uprooted tree at SD 330 995) of dark laminated mudstones of the younger Skelgill Formation, deposited in a deep sea with no bottom-dwelling organisms to disturb the fine laminae.

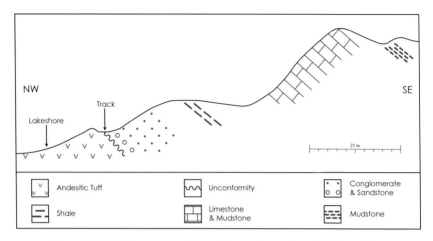

Figure 5. A sketch cross section of the rocks south east of Tarn Hows

Return from Tarn Hows to Tenter Hill (Figure 3), and turn right to High Cross. Cross the Hawkshead-Coniston road and park in the forestry car park 200m further on. Walk back to High Cross, turn left and follow the road for 400m to High Cross Plantation Quarry on the right. Beware of traffic.

Wray Castle Formation	Coniston Group		
Coldwell Formation Birk Riggs Formation Brathay Formation	Tranearth Group	Windermere Supergroup	Silurian
Browgill Formation Skelgill Formation	Stockdale Group		
Dent Group			
- - - - - - - - - - - - - - - Unconformity - - - - - - - - - - - - - - -			Ordovician
Borrowdale Volcanic Group			

Figure 6. The Rock Succession.

Locality 3 (SD 328 985) is High Cross Plantation Quarry. The Brathay Formation crops out in the northwest of the quarry. The large slabs contain buff **siltstone** laminae, small-scale cross-bedding and concretions. A small fault with associated **breccia** is exposed at the northern corner. Walk clockwise around the bottom of the face. Halfway along the northeastern face, paler beds – greywackes of the Birk Riggs Formation, overlie the older, darker Brathay Formation mudstones. These are **proximal turbidites**, deposited in the middle of submarine fans where the continental slope met the deep sea floor. Many beds are graded. Their muddy tops are cleaved but not their sandy bases. Some bed under-surfaces have **flute marks**. *No hammering please!* **Load** and **flame** structures are well developed in a 1m thick bed just south of the eastern corner.

From the car park descend Hawkshead Hill eastwards, turning left past the sawmill at the T-junction at the bottom. Continue along the B5286 past Outgate to a prominent rock-face on the roadside by a right-hand bend 500m later. There is ample parking.

Locality 4 (NY 356 003), on the Outgate-Ambleside roadside shows the younger Wray Castle Formation. A sequence of thick poorly sorted mudstones and greywackes, dipping gently southeast, crops out here. Many beds are about 1m thick with mud to sand-size grains. Some beds show small-scale cross-bedding, capped by parallel laminae with uniform mudstones above. The structures suggest that these rocks are **distal turbidites**, deposited at the outer edges of submarine fans on the deep sea floor. Scratches on some bedding planes, parallel to the dip, suggest that beds have moved against each other during folding.

From Locality 4, cross the road and follow the public footpath parallel to the road, north for 300m to a winding forest track to Coldwell Quarry (disused), east of this path.

Locality 5 (NY 359 010), Coldwell Quarry in the Coldwell Formation is flooded. There are plenty of massive blue-grey, muddy limestones and calcareous siltstones in spoil heaps and exposures on either side of the entrance. The rocks dip south. On a sunny day, **bioturbation**, produced by organisms in and on the sea-floor, may be visible. This formation can be distinguished from the Wray Castle above and the Birk Riggs Formation below by the absence of laminae in the beds. It forms an upstanding ridge as it is relatively resistant to erosion. It has been worked to provide many of the slate slabs set into hedge bases in the Hawkshead area. Quarries and lime kilns are common along its outcrop. Return carefully to the car park.

Walk Number 9

Limestones of the Arnside Area

by Michael Dewey

Purpose	To examine the limestone succession of the Arnside area, with special emphasis on the structure and fossil corals.

Practical Details

Starting Point	Car parking at Arnside shoreline parking area (SD 455 787), with additional parking adjacent to the Kent Viaduct (SD 458 790).
Walk Description	Approx. 8 km walking along public shore line, cliff-top paths and sand bars. The return route has some easy uphill walking. The walk should be undertaken when the tides are low or on the ebb as very high tides cover parts of the route. Tide times are published weekly in the *Westmorland Gazette,* and tide tables are available in Arnside shops, at the Kendal Tourist Information Centre and on the Internet.
Restrictions	Please do not hammer the rocks. Only fossils that are lying loose on the shoreline may be removed.
Maps	1:25,000 Explorer Map OL7. The English Lakes South-eastern area. 1:50,000 Landranger Sheet 97 (Kendal and Morecambe)
Public Transport	Buses are available to Arnside from Milnthorpe and Kendal. There is also a rail service to Arnside.
Public Toilets	In Arnside village near the Kent Viaduct (SD 458 789).
Refreshments	Many cafes and pubs in Arnside.

EXCURSION DESCRIPTION

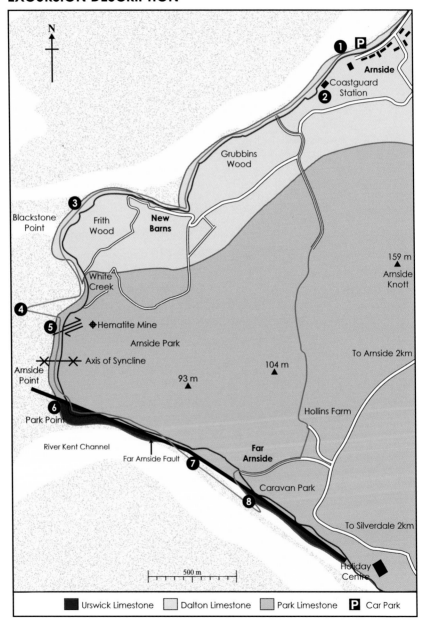

Figure 1. Excursion route.

Follow the shoreline path southwest (left) from the end of the road and car park bays for 200m, then take the steps down to the foreshore.   This is **Locality 1** (SD 452 786). The rocks here are the lowermost **beds** of the Dalton Limestone Formation and contain fossil **brachiopods** called *Delepina carinata.* Take a few minutes to get your eye in, as they can be difficult to see at first. This brachiopod is a useful stratigraphic indicator, (showing where the rocks are in the geological succession) as it is only found in the lower beds of the Dalton Limestone.   In South Cumbria there is a sequence of six distinct limestone deposits in the stages shown in Figure 2. The Dalton and Park limestones seen during this excursion were deposited on a gently sloping ramp in water no deeper than 100m. The shore would have been about 40km to the north, where Keswick is situated today. Each limestone formation differs due to changes in water depth and inputs of clastic material (sand and mud). The limestones were deposited when the land that is now England was about 10° south of the Equator. Each formation ends when sea levels regressed (fell). These changes were caused by movements on large **fault** systems, caused by the northwards movement of Gondwanaland, a supercontinent south of the Equator.

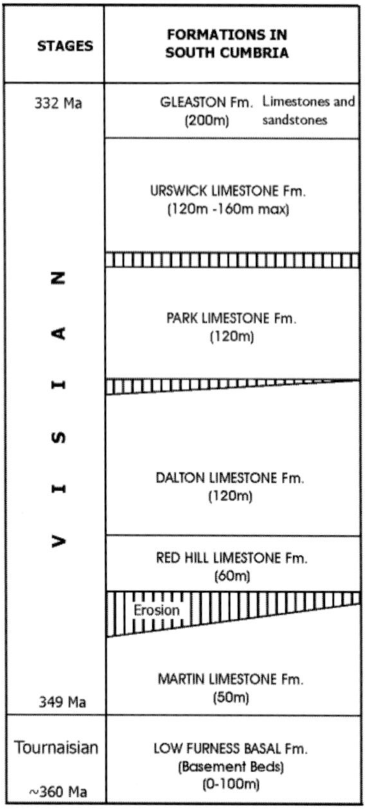

STAGES	FORMATIONS IN SOUTH CUMBRIA	
332 Ma	GLEASTON Fm. (200m)	Limestones and sandstones
	URSWICK LIMESTONE Fm. (120m -160m max)	
	PARK LIMESTONE Fm. (120m)	
V I S E A N	DALTON LIMESTONE Fm. (120m)	
	RED HILL LIMESTONE Fm. (60m)	
	Erosion	
349 Ma	MARTIN LIMESTONE Fm. (50m)	
Tournaisian ~360 Ma	LOW FURNESS BASAL Fm. (Basement Beds) (0-100m)	

Figure 2. Limestone formations of South Cumbria.

Rejoin the path and in a few hundred metres, just past the coastguard station, on your left is **Locality 2** (SD 452 785). The limestone beds here are nearly horizontal and in between there are thinner **shale** (hardened mud) layers. The Dalton Limestone was deposited in deeper water well below wave base. Immediately to the right the limestones are contorted and crumpled by forces from the south. There is also a minor fault, and to the right of this fault the beds are steeply **folded**.

Continue along the coast to Blackstone Point (2km). On the way notice the well-bedded Dalton Limestone dipping to the southwest at about 6°. As you progress you will be going into the younger beds of Dalton Limestone. Walk around the delta shaped salt marsh at New Barns and continue to Blackstone Point, **Locality 3** (SD 437 776). There you will see a magnificent cliff of middle and upper Dalton Limestone containing many fossil **rugose corals** (See Figure 3). In this exposure there are a number of dark shale beds, a characteristic of middle Dalton Limestone. This location has been described as containing the richest Visean fauna of northwest Europe.

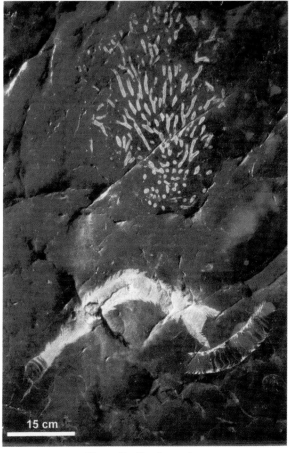

Figure 3. Fossil corals.
(Photo M. Dewey)

Next make your way across the sands bypassing the small bay of White Creek to **Locality 4** (SD 435 771), about 300m from the Arnside Point section of sea-cliff. Look inland and you will see there is a large **syncline** (downward fold) in the cliff. This cliff is in Park Limestone, the next formation up the sequence (see Figure 2) and is paler than the Dalton Limestone, indicating a lack of land derived material. Deposition was in shallow water (10 to 30 metres deep) close to wave base. Walk to the lefthand side of the syncline (west) to see a large fault in the cliff. This is **Locality 5** (SD 437 771). The fault is easily located, as there is a smooth, nearly vertical rock surface in the cliff. It is a good example of a **strike-slip fault** with sideways movement indicated by the presence of horizontal grooves in the vertical rock surface. You can also see that there is a second component to the fault as the beds are offset vertically by about 1.5m. This is a **normal fault**.

Now proceed southwards 300m along the coast to **Locality 6** (SD 437 768), by Park Point just beyond the southern limb of the syncline to another fault in the cliff. This is a major structural feature which I have named the Far Arnside Fault as it controls the shape of the shoreline to Silverdale, a distance of 3km. Looking at the cliff you will see that there are two fault planes, a low angle listric (spoon shaped) fault and a nearly vertical fault (See Figure 4). This is a normal fault with downwards movement of about 150m on the southern side where the younger Urswick Limestone is exposed. Most of the fault movement occurred on the listric fault plane, as this is where the younger Urswick Limestone has been downfaulted. You will see that the fault planes are pink. This is due to **hematite** (a red iron oxide) brought-in by mineralising **hyper saline** fluids, possibly from sandstones in the Irish Sea Basin. Urswick Limestone is also a shallow water sequence. It is strongly bedded and has many beds that have been **bioturbated**, (where the sediment was burrowed by soft bodied creatures such as *Thalassinoides*), producing a rubbly appearance to the bed surfaces. These Urswick Limestone features can be seen at Park Point when you proceed on the cliff-top path to Far Arnside.

Figure 4. Far Arnside Fault.
(Photo M Dewey)

Return the way you came for about 300 metres and walk up the cliff via a well exposed sloping bedding plane to join the cliff-top path. Turn right and proceed to Far Arnside, a distance of 1km to **Locality** 7 (SD 4452 7643). Descend onto the beach to look for a large smooth limestone surface at the western side of Far Arnside Bay. This section of limestone was exposed recently when the River Kent changed position and came nearer to Far Amside, thus causing erosion of the salt marsh. This limestone is the Far Arnside Coral Bed which has many perfectly cross-sectioned rugose corals (See Figure 3). One eminent palaeontologist described the exposure as the best find in thirty years. This type of bed, known as a marine peneplaned hardground (a marine erosion surface), probably formed shortly after deposition when it was scoured by coarse limy sediments. This exposure of the Far Arnside Coral Bed may be covered by a layer of sandy sediments, especially after high tide. Some of the sediment may be removed by washing down with water.

Walk along the shingle for about 200m to **Locality** 8 (SD 447 763) a second fine exposure of the Far Arnside Fault. Look for a channel (or gap between low rock walls) about 2m wide. On the landward side of the channel Dalton Limestone is exposed and on the opposite side Urswick Limestone dips steeply seaward. The Park Limestone, which is 120m thick, is missing here as it has been faulted out. This gives some indication of the scale of movement that has taken place on the fault. Walk over to the sea-cliff, at the bottom section of which is a prominent bed with a wavy surface. This is the junction between the poorly bedded Dalton Limestone and the overlying pale poorly bedded and randomly-**jointed** Park Limestone. Close examination shows a number of fossil corals colonies *(Siphonodendron sp.)* that have been turned upside down. This probably happened during a storm early in lower Carboniferous times.

To return to Arnside go through the gate on the shore that leads through the caravan park and the small hamlet of Far Arnside. Just after the cottages take the stile on the left (way marked) into the field and follow the wall for about 200m to the stile at Hollins Farm. After crossing the stile turn immediately left onto a short track and through the gates. Make your way uphill towards Arnside Knott, pass through another gate into the woods and turn left onto a woodland track that skirts around the hill. After a cattlegrid a tarmac road leads downhill to a T-junction in Arnside village. Turn right at the road junction and after 200m turn left onto a footpath between two houses that goes down to the shoreline. Turn right to the promenade and your starting point.

Walk Number 10

Glacial Deposits on Walney Island

by Derek Leviston

Purpose	To look at glacial deposits of Late Devensian age on Walney Island and discuss their origin and relationship.

Practical Details

Starting Point	The starting point for Locality 1 (1km from parking area) is in a field 300m south of Far South End. The starting point for Localities 2 and 3 is the car park at Thorny Nook, 2km to the localities. The Localities may not be accessible at the highest of tides. There are local Tide Tables and the information is printed in the *North West Evening Mail*.
Walking Description	Easy walking over grass and pebble beach.
Maps	1:25 000 OL6, The English Lakes South-western area.
Public Transport	None.
Public Toilets	None.
Refreshments	Two pubs, The Castle at Bigger Bank and the Queens Arms at Bigger Village.

GEOLOGICAL SETTING

The last major ice advance was between 26 500 and 18 000**BP**. At its peak 20 000 - 18 000BP, the ice cap over the Lake District was probably between 500m and 750m thick.   The Irish Sea Ice Sheet flowed southwards along the west Cumbrian coast from its source on the Dumfries-Galloway peninsula, joining local ice streams flowing west from the Lake District. This ice stream crossed the southern part of the Furness Peninsula to combine with ice streams from the Coniston Fells (See Figure 1). The resulting **tills** (ice deposited material of varying origins, sizes and shapes) contain a mixture of rocks from west Cumbria and the Coniston/Furness Fells.   Red Eskdale **Granite** is a distinctive marker for identifying material deposited by west Cumbria ice.   During deglaciation the Irish Sea Ice stream readvanced over the Furness Peninsula (the Furness Readvance) depositing tills, sands and gravels. Northwest to southeast orientated **drumlins** were formed over Walney Island and the coast near Barrow in Furness.   After the ice retreated erosion followed.   Rivers and streams deposited clays and sands into wide shallow channels.   Periglacial (cold, near glacial) conditions followed resulting in frost heave in the sand and clay, with ice wedges forming in the till deposited during the readvance.   This was followed by the deposition of gravel sheets. The glacial deposits have been divided into two groups, West Cumbria **Drift** Group and South Cumbria Drift Group (Figure 1).

EXCURSION DESCRIPTION

Locality 1 Hare Hill (SD 204 630)   To reach the starting point travel along the tarred road that leads south along Walney Island.   Pass between two parts of South End Caravan site to the ruins of Far South End Farm.   After 200m, turn right off the tarred road along a track which leads to a parking area (SD 205 607) in the field close to the shore.   From the car park proceed to the foreshore and turn north along the shore, passing old wooden sea defences on your left, to Hare Hill which has a lookout tower on the top.   En route the first 1.5m cliff is artificial.   Before reaching the main cliff light grey clay and dark sandy clay containing plant remains of **Flandrian** age may be seen overlying consolidated till.

At Hare Hill it is best to view the section from a distance to obtain an overall impression of the sequence. The middle of the cliff section shows a tripartite sequence of till-sand-till (See Figure 2). The lower till has more **clasts** and is the informally named Hare Hill Till Member. It is a compact lodgement till (deposited at the bottom of the ice sheet). The long axes of the pebbles dip into the cliff and are orientated southwest to northeast.   The great variety of rock types suggest the till was deposited where the Irish Sea Ice Stream met the Lake District Ice Stream from the Coniston and Furness Fells.   The rock types include Carboniferous Limestone, some stained red by iron ore (**hematite**), black **basalt** (many with white spots of minerals), red sandstone, buff coloured sandstone, white vein quartz, green volcanic **agglomerate**, red Eskdale Granite, **ignimbrite**, various sedimentary rocks and volcanic **tuffs** (hardened ash), The clast size ranges from granule (2-4mm diameter) to boulder (over 245mm diameter).   Many of the clasts have good examples of striations (scratch marks) produced by clasts coming into contact with each other during glacial transport.   A 10m deep channel eroded into the till has a thin bed of silt at the base, informally named the South End Silt Bed, which is overlain by massive sand, the informally named

Roose Sand and Gravel Member. **Current bedding** in hard sand at the top of the section (see Figure 2) indicate a **palaeocurrent** flowed west. Examination of the 4.5m high section will reveal various sedimentary features, some outlined by coal particles.

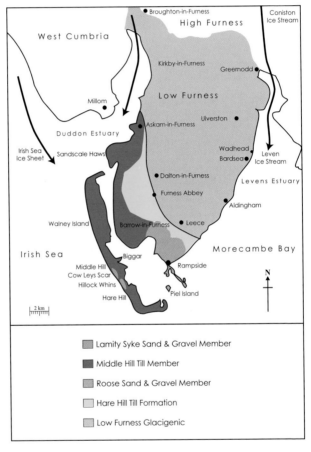

Figure 1. Distribution of Glacial Deposits in Low Furness.

The base of the channel gradually climbs northwards and is cut off by the Middle Hill Till Member (see Locality 2). Follow the section north towards South End (SD 203 632), where the boundary between the Hare Hill Till Member and the overlying Middle Hill Till

Member is marked by an increase in clast density and forms a distinct break in slope in the final 100m of the cliff. The softer, less compact, Middle Hill Till Member is more easily weathered and forms the cliff at beach level near South End.

Locality 2 Middle Hill (SD 1850 6580)   From the car park at Thorny Nook proceed south along the beach to Middle Hill (SD 1850 6580), which forms the first cliffs after the Carboniferous limestone boulders used for sea defences. The till here has a light yellow/brown consolidated sandy clay matrix, supporting clasts ranging in size from granule to boulder. Some clasts show striations, others have rounded tops and flat bases. The flat base was probably produced by the grinding action of the ice, as the clast, frozen to the base of the glacier, moved over the country rock. Shell debris and red, pink and yellow flint, probably from Antrim, may also be found. The varied rocks include ignimbrite, dark **porphyritic** lavas, vein quartz, red Eskdale Granite, grey Criffel Granite, red sandstone, other sedimentary rocks and black basalts. The Irish Sea Ice Stream from Galloway and west Cumbria probably brought these materials. The long axes of the clasts are generally orientated approximately northwest-southeast. This is usually taken to be the direction of glacial flow but does not always agree with that suggested by drumlin orientation. A sandy clay horizon in the upper part of the section is crudely bedded and regular bands of clay horizons about 4cm thick can be seen along the section. The bedding and individual bands represent different rock and sediment types that have been highly attenuated but not mixed during high shear strains produced by glacier movement. This till was deposited during the Furness Readvance and is informally named the Middle Hill Till Member.

Locality 3 Cow Leys Scar (SD 1870 6555) After Middle Hill continue 250m southwards past the limestone sea defences to the low cliffs above Cow Leys Scar. Viewed from a distance the cliff section shows a wide shallow channel eroded into the Middle Hill Till

Member (see Figure 2). A sequence of reddish clays and sands informally named the Cow Leys Sand and Clay Member has been deposited into this channel. The sands occupy the lower part of the section and are coarse grained at the base, grading upwards first into clay with fine sand laminations and then into reddish clays. These are cut by overlying gravels informally named here as the Lamity Syke Sand and Gravel Member. Lines 1, 2 and 3 on the Cow Leys Scar, part of Figure 2, illustrate these deposits.

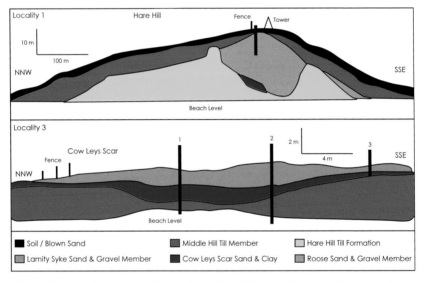

Figure 2. Details of the sections at localities 1 (Hare Hill) and 3 (Cow Leys Scar).

The **foresets** (inclined surfaces) in the laminated clays dip northwards indicate a palaeo-current from that direction. At the south end of the section the Cow Leys Scar Sand and Clay Member is contorted by frost heave and truncated by the overlying gravel.

Another exposure of contorted clay can be seen at (SD 18680 65660) and an example of a frost wedge can be seen at (SD 18686 65589) (Figure 3).

At the north and south ends of the section the gravels rest upon till of the Middle Hill Till Member as the underlying sands and clays thin out.   Rock types in the gravel include red and grey granites, quartz, red sandstone, purple mudstone and siltstones. Foresets in the thin beds of red sand dip in a south-westerly direction suggesting that the source of the pebbles was probably erosion of drumlins located inland of the present coastline. The cliffs extend further southwards where the Lamity Syke Sand and Gravel Member can be seen to make direct contact with the Middle Hill Till Member.

Figure 3. Looking east at a frost wedge in the Middle Hill Till Member.
(Photo D. Leviston)

Walk Number 11

Tilberthwaite

by Geoff Brambles

Purpose	To examine glacial landscapes and the effects of mining and quarrying in the Borrowdale Volcanic Group rocks.

Practical Details

Starting Point	Roadside car park before the bridge below Low Tilberthwaite. (NY 306 010).
Walk Description	A good half day's excursion. Approximately 4km. Rough ground, with a rocky track climbing c. 200m; some boggy areas. Crook Beck to be crossed.
Maps	1:25,000 Explorer OL 6 The English Lakes South-western area. 1:50,000 Landranger Sheet 90 Penrith, Keswick and Ambleside area.
Public Transport	Bus service to Coniston. (Stagecoach, Service 505 from Ambleside, X12 from Ulverston).
Public toilets	None. Nearest are in Coniston.
Refreshments	None.

GEOLOGICAL SETTING

Tilberthwaite lies close to the southeastern limit of the Borrowdale Volcanic Group outcrop. The rocks belong to the later, explosive phase of Ordovician volcanicity, which produced **ignimbrites** and other **pyroclastics**, some of which were reworked into **volcaniclastic** sediments. During the closure of the **Iapetus** Ocean, around 416 **Ma**, these rocks were **folded, faulted, cleaved** and mineralised. The resulting **slates** and metalliferous **veins** have been intensively worked. The evidence of these activities is a key element of the cultural landscape. The general ruggedness is largely the result of glacial erosion, but **drift** deposits add an element of contrasting smoothness. Post-glacial infilling of rock basins is revealed by flat peat mosses.

EXCURSION DETAILS

Locality 1 (NY 306 010) is the bridge over the river, a few yards from the car park (see Figure 1). For about 500m upstream of this point the river follows a fault and has created a deep, steep sided gorge. Downstream, the river turns sharply east, then south, through a short gorge cut into a rock bar, rather than continuing across the flat ground to the northeast. This is an excellent example of glacial diversion of drainage. A pre-glacial col has been breached, either by a tongue of ice, or by meltwater ponded up around Tilberthwaite overflowing and cutting a spillway. The flat ground may be the floor of a former lake dammed by ice.

Locality 2 (NY 307 009) Return past the car park and continue 100m almost to the roadside iron railings. Notice the contrasting use of local stone in Anthony Goldsworthy's sheepfold by Yewdale Beck. Climb the low knoll, Locality 2, to your left, to view the striking contrast between the flat pastures around Tilberthwaite and the gorge below you. Take care as the eastern side of the knoll falls precipitously to Yewdale Beck. 150m along the road turn right towards the ruined buildings and group of spoil heaps 200m to the south. Roadside exposures show slaty cleavage. Leave the road and walk southwest up a track to the stone launder, the flat topped stone ramp that carried water to the waterwheel (1-4 on Figure 2).

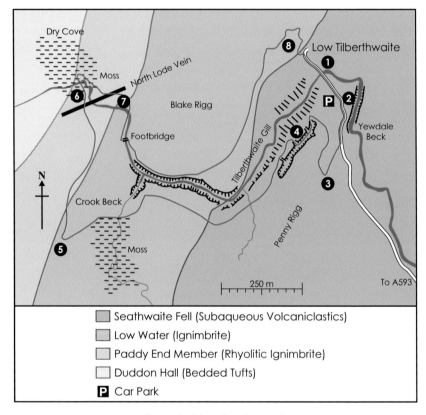

Figure 1. Map showing route.

Locality 3 (NY 306 007) is the remains of Penny Rigg Mill, see Figure 2, which c.1866 – 75 crushed and separated vein ore to obtain copper minerals, mainly chalcopyrite (copper iron sulphide, $CuFeS_2$). The crushers were powered by a 32 foot waterwheel whose wheel pit should be approached cautiously. The wheel was fed by the leat (man made water channel) emerging from the slate tip to the north. The crushed ore was separated from waste material by hand picking, further crushing and finally by gravity settlement in water. All these processes were arranged to use the natural slope of the ground. Fine grains of ore washed out of the mill were trapped in settling ponds beside Yewdale Beck.

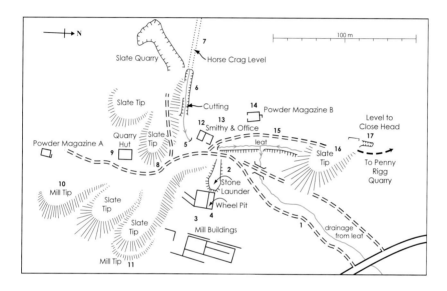

Figure 2. Map of Locality 3.

From the stone launder walk past the ruined smithy and office, through a cutting to the entrance of Horse Crag Level (5-7 on Figure 2). *This can be very wet and slippery.* Do not enter the level, but stand at its entrance and be amazed at this example of the miners' skill and the owners' financial brinksmanship. It is over 900m long, took ten years to complete (c. 1849 – 59) and cost £3,000. Its chief purpose was to drain, and so increase ore output from the lower workings of Tilberthwaite Mine (Locality 7), whose surface buildings are 750m away and 150m higher. However, it was also used for facilitating the transport of ore, using wagons on a tramway, and greatly improved ventilation in the mine. Leave Horse Crag Level and turn right along the track, onto the brownish mill tip with its small samples of sulphide minerals (8-11 on Figure 2).

Walk back past the smithy and office and follow the path north, passing powder magazine B, and onto the mossed over slate tip (12-17 on Figure 2). This slate was extracted in an underground chamber and brought out from the level to a riving shed, (now ruined) where it was split into roofing slates by hand. To the right of the level a path climbs a short, steep slope towards a notch in the fellside. *Take care at the top as you pass close to the end of Penny Rigg Quarry on your left and another quarry on your right.* A short descent leads to a wide, stony path. Turn left onto this path and almost immediately turn left again and pause at the narrow entrance to the quarry.

Locality 4 (NY 305 008) is Penny Rigg Quarry. The steep, slightly overhanging face to the left is a fault plane. This continues on the far side of the quarry as a prominent crack and rusty staining from the leakage of iron-rich groundwater. Enter the quarry. These rocks belong to the Seathwaite Fell Formation and originated as fine-grained volcanic dust that was washed into a lake. After **lithification** into mudstones, they were **metamorphosed** into slate by the immense pressures of the **plate** collision accompanying the closure of the Iapetus Ocean. The remarkable elongated shape of the quarry echoes the northeast-southwest cleavage. The vertical faces are mostly cleavage planes, with **joint** planes causing 'steps' at right angles to the cleavage. The original **bedding** is very difficult to detect. As you walk along the quarry floor, climbing the steep slope of back-filled slate waste, note the old quarry entrance, left high and dry by later quarry deepening. **Frost wedging** has caused some conspicuous collapses.

Stop at the next entrance on the right. Here a **plunging fold** set may reveal the bedding disrupted by an irregular **vein** of milky **quartz** on the right *(see Figure 3)*.

Figure 3. The fold set at locality 4, Penny Rigg Quarry, looking northeast.
(Photo G. Brambles)

Locality 5 describes the route from Penny Rigg Quarry to Wetherlam Mine (NY 297 005). To reach this, follow the main track uphill. Shortly after passing a second abandoned quarry entrance, fork left to continue uphill. For much of the way the path follows a groove that was cut to channel water to the waterwheel at Locality 3. The views into Tilberthwaite Gill are spectacular. As the gradient eases, the closely spaced cleavage planes of the Seathwaite Fell Formation are replaced by the more massive Low Water Ignimbrite. This is most easily examined in the spoil tip of a small level, where a barren vein was explored. After another 250m the path curves round towards Crook Beck, with the high ground of the Coniston Fells rising sharply to the west. Before crossing Crook Beck, locate a group of timber posts about 250m to the southwest, at the foot of the steeply rising ground beyond the beck. Skirt the peat moss towards the posts. The moss is a waterlogged, peat filled, glacially eroded basin. The timber posts mark the site of the short-lived Wetherlam Mine, which worked one of the veins crossing the ground between here and Tilberthwaite Mine (Locality 7).

From here good examples of glacial landforms can be seen. To the north, Blake Rigg and its neighbours are typical of the steep sided, rocky knolls sculpted beneath flowing ice. They are characteristic of the lower fells. To the east, the ground is less rugged and consists of gently sloping, **erratic**-strewn **moraine** and **roches moutonnées.**

Locality 6 (NY 297 010) is Dry Cove. To reach this, follow the path north, skirting the steep slopes to your left, until you reach the low waterfalls near Tilberthwaite Mine. Look for small workings on four veins crossing the slopes on your left. These all contain milky quartz stringers, and one has visible chalcopyrite (copper sulphide). Passing Tilberthwaite Mine on your right, walk a short distance into Dry Cove Bottom. This is the floor of a **cîrque** (locally cîrques are called 'coves'), one of a group of six that developed on the eastern flank of the Coniston Fells. Steel Edge is the southern **arête,** Wetherlam Edge and Birk Fell the northern. The peat moss of Dry Cove Bottom probably occupies the site of an infilled shallow cirque lake. The modern beck flows over the cirque threshold, where the bedrock, a **rhyolitic** ignimbrite (The Paddy End Member), is exposed as a pale grey, flinty looking rock with an interesting texture of short, interlocking fractures.

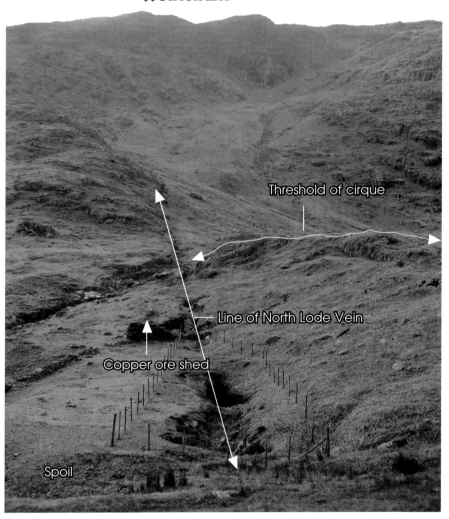

Figure 4
The open workings on the North Lode vein, locality 7, looking west-southwest.
(Photo G. Brambles)

Locality 7 (NY 299 009) is Tilberthwaite Mine. The most dramatic feature here is the ancient line of elongated, open pits on the North Lode vein *(Figure 4)*. These are at least 400 years old. The small building adjacent was the copper (ore) shed and the one beside the tumbled wall housed a wheel pit, smithy and office. This mine was worked sporadically from at least late Elizabethan times until about 1930. The eastern tip contains numerous specimens of green copper minerals.

Locality 8 (NY 305 011) is Low Tilberthwaite, about 1km away. To reach here follow the beck downstream to the footbridge and climb the sloping path to the well graded stony track that leads down to Low Tilberthwaite. This is an old mine road which served all the mines around Dry Cove. It gives excellent views of Tilberthwaite Gill and the spoil heaps of Penny Rigg Quarry.

At Low Tilberthwaite examine the buildings for the many uses to which the slaty Seathwaite Fell Formation has been put. Turn right onto the road to the car park 100m beyond.

Walk Number 12

Wasdale Head

by David Livesey

Purpose	To look at volcanic and igneous rocks at Wasdale Head and how the scenery has been shaped during and after recent ice ages.

Practical Details

Walk Description	Fairly easy walking of around 5km along the valley bottoms. One or two short uphill sections. Boots advisable.
Starting Point	Large parking area at Wasdale Head (NY187 086).
Maps	1:25 000 OL6 English Lakes South western area. 1:50 000 BGS Sheet 36.
Public Transport	No regular public transport up Wasdale.
Public Toilets	None except when taking refreshments.
Refreshments	At the inn at Wasdale Head and also in Nether Wasdale.

GEOLOGICAL SETTING

Wasdale Head is about 2km² of level ground enclosed by mountains at the head of Wastwater. It is an alluvial plain divided by cobblestone walls into irregular-shaped, cultivated enclosures which probably date from Norse times. The area was extensively shaped by ice which was present in great thickness and which disappeared less than18 000**BP**. Glaciers which flowed south and west over the area, or fast flowing ice streams under an immensely thick ice sheet, carved out the valley now occupied by Lingmell Beck   It also formed the **hanging valley** of Mosedale and scooped out the perched combe of Hollowstones, high above Wasdale Head, from which tumbles Lingmell Gill. A much shorter cold period 11 - 10 000BP probably resulted in local glaciers existing only in Mosedale, in the high hollows below Sty Head and under the cliffs of Scafell.

The mountains surrounding Wasdale Head consist of **lavas** and **tuffs** of the Borrowdale Volcanic Group produced 460 - 450**Ma** during the Upper Ordovician Period (Figure 1). Volcanic rocks around Wasdale Head were produced in two distinct phases. The first, relatively quiet phase gave rise to a thick (3km) series of andesitic lava flows, the Birker Fell Formation. A second, more violent phase ejected large quantities of **acidic, pyroclastic** material made up of **rhyolites** and **dacites**, rock types that contain more silica than the andesites. These formed the Scafell Caldera succession. In Wasdale the andesitic rocks underlie the valley floor and outcrop on the lower slopes of the encircling mountains, Yewbarrow, Lingmell, Scafell and Ill Gill Head.   The andesites are present right to the top of Kirkfell. The Scafell Caldera succession lies **unconformably** on the Birker Fell Formation and is found along the summit ridge of Yewbarrow, on all of Great Gable and on the upper slopes of Lingmell, Scafell and Ill Gill Head (Figure 1).   This is a simplified description. The Birker Fell Formation contains some beds of rocks of explosive origin and some lavas are found in the Scafell Caldera succession.

EXCURSION DESCRIPTION

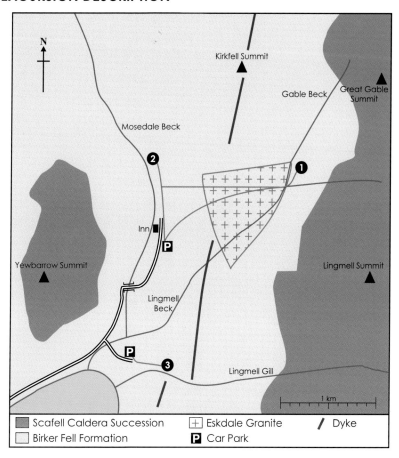

Figure 1. Excursion Map.

From the car park (NY 187 087) walk past the church, almost hidden by its yew trees. The field walls are mainly of rounded cobbles. The darker ones are of **andesitic** lava from the first period of volcanic activity; the paler coloured cobbles are of more acidic rocks, belonging to the subsequent phases of activity. An occasional flatter piece indicates a tuff (consolidated volcanic ash). The network of walls is a testimony to the use made of the vast amount of eroded material carried down into the valley by ice and water during the last few thousand years. Indeed, the smooth lower slopes of the surrounding fells show how much debris still covers the underlying rocks. Should another ice age come almost all of this material would be removed relatively easily from the valley sides.

From a little further on along the lane towards Burnthwaite Farm the slopes of Lingmell to the right can be viewed. Above the lower slopes, a series of low crags slant gently downward to the left, (northeast). This stepped relief is commonly seen on Lakeland fells. Where the rocks **dip** at a low angle, as here, the resistant lavas form near-vertical rock faces and the less resistant **volcaniclastic** rocks weather readily to form benches. Lingmell Crag, prominent on the eastern skyline, consists of a tough dacite lava. During the last minor glaciation ice formed the small combe below Sty Head. In good weather this combe is visible from near Burnthwaite Farm. Small terminal **moraines** outline the lip of the combe. The barn walls at the farm display the variety of texture in the volcanic rocks and their value as local building material.

Continue to **Locality 1**, the footbridge over Gable Beck (NY 199 093), (Figure 1). The prominent Napes ridges high on Great Gable are formed of the same dacite lava as is Lingmell Crag facing them across the valley. From the footbridge an extensive area of pale brown slabs is clearly visible in the stream bed. Walk for a few tens of metres up the east side of the beck and step down on to this massively **jointed** rock. This is the Eskdale **Granite**, part of a deep-seated **intrusion** underlying much of south-western Lakeland, emplaced after the Borrowdale Volcanic Group erupted, but still in Ordovican times. Gravitational surveys show the granite is in the form of a **batholith** which is in contact with the volcanic rocks beneath the Wasdale region at a depth of less than 2km. This exposure in Gable Beck is probably a small intrusion which has risen from the upper surface of the batholith.

Continue up the beck until about fifty metres before the wall the granite disappears beneath the andesite which it had intruded. Neither the intrusive nor the volcanic rock appears to have been altered by one another at this junction. A further few metres up the beck two or three quartz veins cross the stream bed. A small offset, or discontinuous displacement of a few centimetres in each vein indicates minor **faulting** along the line of the beck. As you return to the footbridge visit the large boulder, on the western side of Gable Beck. It is composed of large angular fragments indicating it is a **breccia**, possibly formed in a violent eruption. .

Walk back to Burnthwaite, passing behind the farm buildings to follow the little Fog Mire Beck which runs below moraine heaps lying under Kirkfell, until you meet the path descending from Mosedale. Turn right, pass through two gates and continue for about 300m. Now look over the wall at Mosedale Beck cascading down a rock step (Ritson's Force) in the Birker Fell Formation as it flows out of the hanging valley of Mosedale, (Figure 1). The ice which filled the valley of Lingmell Beck as it descended from Sty Head continued to cut down its bed, after the thinner Mosedale ice had lost its erosive power. A little further along the path the top of a rise is *Locality 2* (NY 184 096) with a good view into Mosedale. Mosedale also had a small glacier in the last short-lived minor glacial advance 11 - 10 000BP. It is interesting to compare the desolate, ill-drained floor of Mosedale, littered with moraine heaps, with the inhabited, comparatively fertile Wasdale Head seen behind and below. Wasdale Head (Figure 2) has better drainage and is on a through route to Borrowdale.

Figure 2. Wasdale Head.
(Photo W. Stainton)

Walk back to the car park. On Yewbarrow rocks belonging to the Scafell Caldera Succession are downfaulled into the older Birker Fell Formation rocks.

Proceed to the National Trust car park at the head of the lake where a gravel delta is being built out into the lake (NY182 075). From here walk to the bridge over Lingmell Gill, turn left up a rough path on the south side of the stream to a footbridge, **Locality 3**, (NY 186 073), reached after about 350m. A prominent **dyke** outcrops about 3m above the bridge (Figure 3). This dyke is 3-5m wide and is pink on the north bank but brick red in the stream. A piece of it with 1-2cm crystals of **plagioclase** (rectangular and white) and quartz forms part of the steps to the bridge. The dyke is a quartz-feldspar, granite **porphyry**; with quartz and feldspar crystals set in a fine groundmass.

Figure 3. Quartz porphyry dyke below footbridge over Lingmell Gill.
(Photo M. Dodd)

The dyke can be intermittently traced over Kirkfell summit from near Black Sail Pass to the vicinity of the granite exposure in Gable Beck, visited earlier in the excursion. It reappears here at Lingmell Gill and continues to the top of Ill Gill Head (NY170 050) before meeting the Eskdale Granite at Great Bank (NY144 018), a total distance of 12km. This dyke is thought to have formed soon after the Eskdale Granite, with which it is most likely associated. The dyke can be examined more closely, on returning down the gill to the climbing club hut, by taking the path leading to Burnmoor Tarn. The dyke will be met after about 1km where it runs for a short distance along the path.

Before finally returning to the car park look towards the lake as you cross the bridge below the climbing club hut. A fan-shaped area (NY 182 070), now much covered by gorse, stretches to the lake. This area of large and ill-sorted boulders was formed during a massive downpour in August 1938 when Lingmell Gill became a devastating torrent, sweeping a heavy load of material down from Hollow Stones.

Walk Number 13

St. Bees

by David Kelly

Purpose	To examine the St Bees Sandstone, the glacial and glaciofluvial sediments on the coast at St Bees.

Practical Details

Starting Point	Sea front car park (NX 961 118) at St Bees (pay and display).
Walk Description	Approximately 5.5 km. One steep section (optional) to Locality 1. The excursion should be completed at low tide if Localities 3 and 7 are to be visited. Tide tables are available locally and on the Internet. Weekly details are given in the *Whitehaven News*.
Maps	1:25 000 Explorer Map 303, Whitehaven and Workington. 1:50 000 Landranger 89 West Cumbria.
Public Transport	St Bees railway station is 1 km from the starting point at the car park. Buses from Whitehaven available.
Public Toilets	At the car park start point.
Refreshments	Café adjacent to the car park. Pubs in St Bees.

GEOLOGICAL SETTING

The outcrop of the over 200**Ma** Triassic St Bees Sandstone Formation underlies the west coast of Cumbria south from St Bees to Barrow in Furness. This excursion visits one of its few exposures. Complex magnetic evidence indicates that the rock was formed when Britain lay in latitudes similar to the Sahara Desert of today. Although the climate was arid, occasional torrential rainstorms caused flash floods, which transported vast amounts of sediment. The St. Bees Sandstone was deposited by such floods, which swept across broad plains carrying sediment eroded from the mountains that lay across southwest Britain and northwest France. The rock forms St Bees Head, the last major coastal cliff in a southward direction before the Great Orme in North Wales. The rock has been used in the construction of many of the older buildings in south and west Cumbria. The rarity of exposures is partly due to the thick **glacial drift** over most of the coastal plain. At St Bees, this drift cover is exposed in coastal cliffs. This excursion is entirely along the Cumbria Coastal Way footpath or on the foreshore.

EXCURSION DESCRIPTION

Locality 1 (NX 952 122) is the viewpoint constructed from a World War Two coastguard lookout on St Bees South Head, also known as Tomlin. This is reached by walking about 1km up the cliff path at the northwest end of the concrete promenade, to a height of 90m above sea level. Approaching the viewpoint, notice the aligned, often vegetated, cliff-top craters known as the Pattering Holes. These seem to be an area of landslips along open **joints** in the bedrock. A few metres north of the viewpoint is a small, disused sandstone quarry in St. Bees Sandstone, see Figure 2. The small-scale **current bedding** in this sandstone indicates it was waterlain. The **beds** here are up to a metre thick; the **dip** is very gentle and not easy to determine. The old field boundaries, conspicuous on the cliff edge and inland, date from the enclosures of the early nineteenth century.

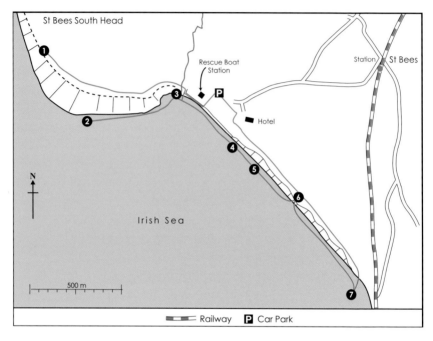

St Bees South Head

Rescue Boat Station

Station St Bees

Hotel

N

Irish Sea

500 m

Railway   P Car Park

Figure 1 Excursion route.

Return to the promenade, but on the way pause to view the valley running northeast linking St Bees with Whitehaven. The valley is drained by Pow Beck, and was probably eroded by glacial meltwater. It is far too large to have been formed by the present day stream. Therefore Pow Beck is termed a 'misfit' stream. The seaward end of the valley is blocked by glacial and **glaciofluvial** deposits forming low sea cliffs, which will be seen later in the excursion at Localities 5 and 6.

Figure 2. Current bedding in St. Bees Sandstone at Locality 1.

(Photo M. Dodd)

Locality 2 (NX 958 116) is the foot of the cliff immediately north of the outflow of Rottington Beck. It can be reached from the north end of the Promenade. Here there is a deposit of poorly sorted cobbles, gravel and sand, thought to be a **morainic** deposit. See Figure 3. This is the Lowca **Till**, deposited by an ice sheet in the last main glaciation (the Devensian). The cobbles are mostly St. Bees Sandstone, but you will also find 300 Ma sandstones, shales, coals and 450+Ma Borrowdale Volcanic Group rocks.

Locality 3 (NX 957 117) is the wave-cut platform and cliffs at the foot of St Bees South Head. It is only accessible at low tide and care should be taken on the slippery rocks. By walking as far as the old swimming pool carved in the rock, you can see the Triassic St Bees Sandstone in beds dipping gently to the south-southwest. The St Bees Sandstone is a uniform, fine-grained, **micaceous**, reddish brown sandstone deposited in flash floods by temporary streams in an arid environment.

*Figure 3. Lowca Till at Locality 2. Notice boulders
of varied size in a fine-grained matrix.*

(Photo D. Powell)

Three types of sedimentary structures can be seen. Firstly, some beds show strong parallel **laminations**. This was formed when strong currents transported sand grains in fairly shallow water. Secondly, there are excellent examples of **cross-bedding,** formed by weaker currents in sandbanks in the river channels. The dip of the cross-bedding shows the directions of the currents which deposited the sands. Here the dips of the bedding are generally towards the north or northeast, indicating current flows from the south and southwest. Thirdly, you may also see examples of ripple marks, due to very weak currents which formed sandbanks in the stream channels. The long side of the ripples face north or northeast reflecting a current flowing from that direction. The red colour of the sandstone is caused by hematite (a red iron oxide) between the sand grains, deposited in desert or semi-desert conditions. If you are able to see a bedding plane surface of the sandstone you will notice that it glistens with flakes of **mica**. Although many red desert sandstones form in wind-blown dunes, the presence of the mica indicates that these sandstones have been deposited by water. In water, the buoyant mica flakes settle slowly from suspension to rest on top of the sand, but the winnowing action of transport by wind tends to remove the mica flakes.

Locality 4. (NX 962 116) is at the southeast end of the concrete promenade. Here boulders of Carboniferous Limestone from a quarry in west Cumbria have been used to create sea defences. A search in the boulders will reveal examples of fossil **brachiopods** and colonial corals. In front of the sea defences and close to the high tide level is a 3m long boulder of green rock from the Borrowdale Volcanic Group. This is a glacial **erratic**, often partly buried by shingle. It was eroded from its natural outcrop by ice, transported and deposited here at St. Bees. The pebbles and cobbles of the storm beach show a great variety of rock types transported by ice from the north and west of Cumbria and the south of Scotland. Although there are some pieces of the St Bees Sandstone, harder rocks are more common. Many of the blue and green pebbles are from the Borrowdale Volcanic Group, sometimes with small crystals visible. Pieces of orange/ pink Ennerdale **Granophyre** are also common.

Locality 5 (Between NX 965 114 and NX 969 108) is the low cliff below St Bees golf course, formed from glacial and glaciofluvial material. These deposits are complex and their interpretation has proved controversial. There are two deposits to identify. One is a glacial till at the base of the cliffs: this is a sticky, reddish, unbedded clay which contains small pebbles. This is the St. Bees Till, slightly younger than the Lowca Till seen at locality 2. The second type of deposit (overlying the till) was laid down by water and ranges from sand to gravel to boulders. Bedding is well developed in the sands and is sometimes made conspicuous by lines of coal fragments. The coarser deposits are poorly bedded and include boulders, often of St Bees Sandstone, which must have been transported by torrential flows of water.

The deposits found in the cliff have been **folded**, possibly by pressure from a late re-advance of the Scottish ice from the northwest, suggesting there was a third ice advance at St. Bees. This is best seen by looking back at the cliff from the sandy beach at low tide. The cliffs are constantly changing due to coastal erosion but examples of the folding can be seen about 200 metres southeast of the end of the sea defences.

Locality 6 (NX 965 113) is at the top of the cliff. It can be reached by a muddy scramble up either of the grassy, slumped area of cliff. Alternatively, it can be left until the return walk along the cliff top. The point can be easily identified, as it is 100m southeast of the well-signposted 9th tee on the golf course and near a green. Here a pale clay separates two layers of peat. Dating using pollen and ^{14}Carbon indicates an age of 11 000 to 13 000 years before present, in the Windermere **Interstadial**. This has been interpreted as a **kettle hole** deposit, which formed when a huge block of ice became isolated from the main ice sheet and was buried or surrounded by deposits from meltwater streams. When the isolated block of ice eventually melted a hollow was left in which a small tarn or pool may have formed.

Locality 7 (NX 968 107), visible at low tide near an old sewage outfall just beyond the end of the cliffs at Seamill, is an exposure of tree stumps and roots in grey clay. Take care, the rocks can be very slippery here. This is part of one of several submerged forests along the coast of Cumbria and probably dates from about 8 000 **BP**. Here Pow Beck flows out of the St Bees – Whitehaven valley and into the sea.

Return to the car park by walking along the Cumbria Coastal

Way path along the cliff top (visiting Locality 6) or walk along the road under the railway bridge which leads to St Bees Village. The cliff top walk affords excellent views north-eastwards to the St Bees - Whitehaven valley.

Walk Number 14

Cycleway at Frizington

by Mervyn Dodd

Purpose	To look at rocks exposed around the Cycleway and at old iron mines nearby.

Practical Details

Walk Description	4-5km walk, partly along the tarmacked Cycleway, partly along paths, rough and muddy in places, less than 50m ascent.
Starting Point	The end of Yeathouse Road, Frizington where Winder Gate begins (NY 040 172).
Maps	1:25 000 Explorer 303 Whitehaven and Workington. 1:25 000 OL4 The English Lakes North-western area. 1:50 000 Landranger Sheet 89 West Cumbria.
Public Transport	Bus from Whitehaven. Alight at the Methodist Church opposite Yeathouse Road which you follow for ¾ km to the starting point. Roadside parking by the starting point.
Public Toilets	None.
Refreshments	Café at the Lingla Centre, St. Pauls Church, Frizington, serves weekday lunches. The Old New Griffin pub, The Square, Frizington.

GEOLOGICAL SETTING

Historically the iron oxide **hematite** (Fe_2O_3) has been a very important mineral in West Cumbria. It occurs irregularly in relatively small ore bodies, often near **faults** (fractures in the rock along which there has been displacement), in the Carboniferous Limestone beds. Hematite is a dark cherry red, hard, high grade iron ore, sometimes kidney shaped, virtually phosphorus free and was typically 55-60% iron content. It was in great demand for the Bessemer steel making process, which was used after 1858. Large scale hematite mining developed in West Cumbria, booming in the 1880s before a long slow decline began with large scale operations ending in the 1970s, as newer processes were developed that were less particular about ore quality. Its irregular occurrence made hematite difficult to find and expensive to mine, often being worked 300m below the surface.

The Yeathouse Fault, Figure 1, shows the three main types of ore body in the iron mines: the '**veins**' following the steep fault planes; the 'flats' running along the beds of limestone and the irregular vugs which sometimes fill caves in the limestone.

EXCURSION DETAILS

Locality 1, (NY 041 172), is reached by walking down the track past the Yeathouse Farm buildings for about 20m to a metal gate on your right (west), see Figure 3. The ground to the left (east) has been landscaped over the remains of the small Yeathouse Mine. These shallow pits (60m deep), first leased in 1745, were worked for the iron and steel works in West Cumbria. The quarry to the right (west) is in the thick beds of the Eskett Limestone of the Great Scar Limestone Group of the lower Carboniferous, about 330 - 340**Ma** (Figure 2).

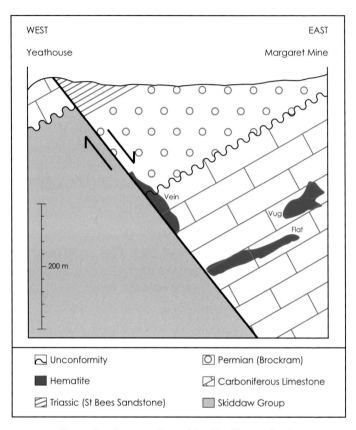

Figure 1.   Cross-section of the Yeathouse Fault.

Period	Rock Formation	Age
Triassic	St. Bees Sandstone	over 200Ma
Permian	Breccia	300-250Ma
U N C O N F O R M I T Y		
Carboniferous	Eskett Limestone Frizington Limestone Marsett Formation	330 - 350Ma
U N C O N F O R M I T Y		
Ordovician	Buttermere Formation	470Ma

Figure 2. Sequence of rocks in the Frizington area.

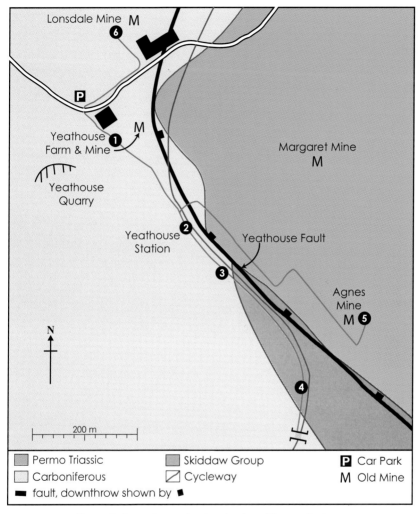

Figure 3. Excursion route showing localities and mines.

These limestones were deposited in clear, shallow, warm, tropical seas, rather like the Caribbean today. The track here follows the line of the northwest to southeast trending Yeathouse fault, hidden by **glacial drift**. Boreholes show that the fault has dropped the area to the east (left) by about 300m, bringing the red desert St. Bees Sandstone (Triassic, over 200Ma) against the much older

Carboniferous Limestone, See Figure 1. Continue down the track, rather rough and damp here, for about 350m, walking under the Cycleway bridge. The walls of the underpass are dressed blocks of the St. Bees Sandstone, much used for building in West Cumbria. Look for blocks with small scale **cross-bedding,** characteristic of waterlain sediments. Pitting of the surface, is a characteristic of this rock which reduces the quality of the stone. Turn right onto the Cycleway by Yeathouse station platforms.

Locality 2 (NY 043 169), is Yeathouse Station on what was the Whitehaven, Cleator and Egremont railway line, which served the local iron mines. The yellow bricks of the station platforms came from the Great Clifton brickworks near Workington. As you continue down the Cycleway into the cutting, the Frizington Limestone, the oldest local limestone, is exposed on the right (west). This is reddened by hematite and gives way in places to much softer beds of shale (hardened muds). Trace fossils (e.g. tracks of ancient animal life) are common on the underside of some of the thick limestone beds. Some of the mosses growing below the limestone are coated in **calcite**, deposited by water enriched in this mineral, seeping out of the rock.

Locality 3, (NY 043 168), is 80m further down the track. There is an opening to the right (west). This is a failed "trial" to look for ore, excavated between 1880 and 1890 when the railway was at its busiest. You can see here the, **dip** westwards into the trial (Figure 4) and the **strike** (at right angles to the dip) of the rocks very clearly in the entrance.

Figure 4. Failed trial in the Frizington Limestone.
(Photo S. Beale)

15m or so further down the track on the left (east) are 3m high screes of pale bleached fragments of rock. Thin outcrops of shale slope steeply north towards Yeathouse station. These shales belong to the Buttermere Formation of the Ordovician Skiddaw Group, at 470Ma the oldest rock in Cumbria – at least 120 million years older than the limestones. The Skiddaw rocks were laid down in a deep ocean. There is an **unconformity** here beneath the Cycleway, representing a break in deposition after the Buttermere Formation. The unconformity is an irregular surface which rises to the left (east) and above the track in front of us. 10m or so to the right (west) is a small sandy yellowish patch of rock, not always visible in summer, with a 1m arch of dark rock above. These are the Basement Beds of the Carboniferous, now called the Marsett Formation. Continue down the track for about 100m, passing

Skiddaw Group rocks, which vary greatly in bed thickness and generally slope steeply north towards Yeathouse station.

Locality 4, (NY 046 165) is a stone bench above which deeply rotted Skiddaw Group rocks are easy to examine. Immediately above the bench the alternating thick and thin beds show these are **turbidites**, rocks deposited by intermittent submarine currents of varying strength. In the 50m or so to the end of the cutting before the red St. Bees Sandstone farm bridge, individual beds are contorted, especially to the left of the track. These contortions are **slump folds** which may have formed when sediments, freshly deposited on the sea floor, were suddenly moved by earth tremors.

Turn back before the farm bridge and retrace your footsteps to Yeathouse station. Leave the Cycleway, turning down the track to the right (south) on the second bend to take a path beside the Windergill stream. Follow this path, narrow in places, for about 175m, almost as far as "The Boilers", an aqueduct or pipeline carrying the stream water to prevent it flooding the Margaret and other mines while they were being worked. A narrow, steep, rough path leads up the side of the tips (where samples of hematite, **quartz** and **dolomite** can be found) to the flat terrace of the long-gone railway to the Margaret Mine, (1880-1923, 300m deep), the largest local iron ore mine. Follow this terrace (right) east for about 130m to pass small, sometimes overgrown exposures of the rarely seen brockram to your left (north). Brockrams are reddened **breccias** (layers of coarse gravel), deposited in the Permian period, Figure 3, (250 to 300Ma) during flash floods on desert landscapes. The gravels consist of partly rounded limestone and volcanic pebbles, usually 2-5cms long. The outcrop of the brockram beds slope gently down towards the northwest. Continue eastwards along this path, overgrown in places, for about 100m.

Locality 5, (NY 048 165), the remains of the Agnes Mine complex (1850-1923).   Traces of an old wheel pit and the footings of a small building can be seen on the valley side above Windergill Beck.   A 1m thick exposure of the brockram outcrops above a retaining wall near the wheel pit.   On the valley floor are the remains of a larger building (20m x 15m) with a low tip of clinker at least 20m x 5m in extent.   There are few other remains of old iron mine buildings in West Cumbria.   This small, shallow mine was mothballed after production ceased in 1874 but served as a pumping shaft for the larger, deeper and more efficient Margaret Mine.   Return to Yeathouse Road.   For a short extra walk, turn right (east) along Winder Gate for about 100m.   Turn left (north) by the first house and go about 220m along a track and path into a field.

Locality 6, (NY 043 177), is a small, low tip.   This is Lonsdale No 3 pit, part of the Lonsdale Mine (1874-1924, 220m deep), which worked different limestone beds.   Small fresh looking samples of hematite kidneys, clear and white pyramidal quartz with triangular faces, creamy dolomite with curved faces, tabular **barite**, sometimes unexpectedly blue, and less often, brassy **pyrite** can be found here. Retrace you footsteps to the starting point.

Walk Number 15

Honister and Haystacks

by Hugh Tuffen

Purpose	To look at Borrowdale Volcanic Group rocks. A visit to the Honister Slate Mine is highly recommended.

Practical Details

Starting point	Car park at the summit of Honister Pass (NY 225 136).
Walk description	Honister Pass to Haystacks return is 7.5 km with 325m ascent, moderate to hard. Strong footwear and windproof clothing essential.
Maps	1:25 000 OL4, The English Lakes North western area. 1: 50 000 Landranger Sheet 89 West Cumbria area, or Sheet 90 Penrith, Keswick and Ambleside area. 1:50 000 BGS Sheet 29 (Keswick). Wainwright, A Pictorial Guide to the Lakeland Fells, Book 7, the Western Fells.
Public Transport	Regular summer bus service from Keswick and Cockermouth.
Public Toilets	At Honister Slate Mine.
Refreshments	Tea and coffee at Honister Slate Mine.

GEOLOGICAL SETTING

The dramatic landscapes around Honister and Haystacks are the product of a geologically "brief" volcanic episode 460 - 450**Ma**. At first eruptions were "relatively quiet". The Lower Borrowdale Volcanic Group rocks consist of many **andesitic** lavas and substantial thicknesses of **volcaniclastic** sediments which were deposited in lakes. The interaction of hot lavas and cold lake water may have triggered explosive eruptions. Together these events created an andesitic plateau, later covered by the widespread **pyroclastic** deposits from the very violent eruptions which resulted in the collapse of the Scafell **Caldera**. At the head of the Buttermere valley there are many different volcanic rock types exposed above the **unconformable** contact with the older Skiddaw Group Rocks. The excursion will visit an andesite **lava** dome and lava flow (on Haystacks) together with the volcanic **breccias** (rock fragments) derived from these rocks and deposited in a shallow lake nearby. We will also encounter andesitic **sills** that intruded rather thicker volcaniclastic sediments and generated distinctive **peperitic textures** on Fleetwith Pike.

EXCURSION DETAILS

The excursion starts with a highly scenic walk, from Honister Pass to the summit of Haystacks (allow about an hour). The locations visited are described on the return journey from Haystacks. Take the footpath from Honister Slate Mines, signposted Haystacks and Great Gable. This joins the old mine tramway, at first climbing an inclined plane. Follow this track to the old mine workings and continue on the well-marked footpath to Haystacks summit.

Locality 1 (NY 193 132) is the summit area of Haystacks, which consists of the flow-banded upper portion of a 300m or so thick dome of fine-grained andesite lava (the Haystacks Andesite). The lava has distinctive flow structures picked out by curved fractures formed by shearing and contraction during the cooling of the lava. Explore the summit to see these. Notice that many **folds** trend northeast to southwest indicating compression at 90° to the lines of the folds i.e. in a northwest to southeast direction.

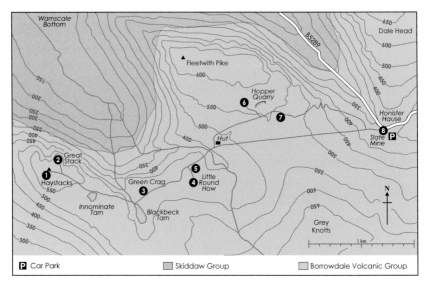

Figure 1. Excursion map.

Open folds with wavelengths of 2m trending northeast to southwest are seen at the more northerly of two summit cairns on the rocky ridge southeast of a small tarn (NY 1933 1320). These are best viewed from across the tarn. Much tighter V-shaped folds are to be found fifty metres to the southwest (NY 1932 1315). Elsewhere on the rocky summit ridge smaller-scale buckling can be found on the folds indicating complex compressional folding on a range of scales.

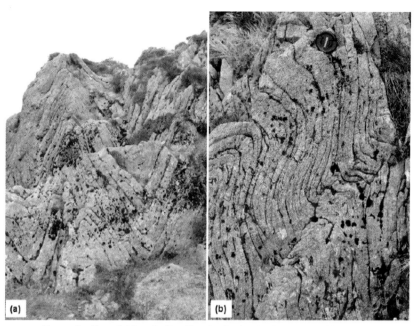

Figure 2. Flow folding in the Haystacks Andesite at (NY 1932 1315).
(a) Tight V-shaped folds with a ~2 m wavelength.
(b) Smaller-scale buckle folds; lens cap is 62 mm across.
(Photo H. Tuffen)

From the northern summit cairn of Haystacks take the path descending eastwards for 100m, with a small scramble, and then follow the faint track that branches left to the crest of a prominent rocky promontory, called Great Stack.

Locality 2 (NY 1939 1320) is the top of Great Stack where this folded flow banding in the lava is well developed. The great thickness of the lava makes up the entire precipitous north face of Haystacks. The rounded outcrops of the gentler slopes of Warnscale Bottom far below are the underlying Skiddaw Group rocks. In good visibility Great Stack provides a fine view of the western face of Fleetwith Pike, where Honister slate of the Borrowdale Volcanic Group rests unconformably upon Skiddaw Group rocks. The lower part of the southeast dipping Honister slates crops out as the steep cliffs of

Striddle Crag. To the south and east the striped ground reflects the alternation of andesitic sills and volcaniclastic sediments, the latter eroding more easily than the sills in this thick sequence. The sediments have been mined for Honister slate, as seen on the slope between Striddle Crag and Hopper Quarry. Return to the main path and continue eastwards, passing Innominate Tarn and Blackbeck Tarn.

Locality 3 (NY 2027 1300) is where the path passes south of the prominent small peak of Green Crag, about 150m after crossing Black Beck. Here we encounter strongly **cleaved**, poorly-sorted fragmental volcanic rocks (breccias). These breccias contain angular clasts of andesite lava up to 20cm long within a pebbly sandstone matrix. The breccias are thought to have formed in a shallow lake at the foot of the lava bodies, where fragments cascading from the upper surface of the lava mixed with fine-grained volcanic ash. A detour to the small summit of Green Crag is well worthwhile for the excellent view of Haystacks, Fleetwith and the Buttermere Valley.

Locality 4 (NY 2067 1315) is on the western side of Little Round How, where the Round How Breccias are well exposed. Continue eastwards from Green Crag for about 300m until you cross a stream draining a boggy depression just west of the rocky outcrop of Little Round How. Follow this stream (no path) for 100m southwards to a pile of boulders at the foot of a crag. Above the boulders is a south-facing rock face about 5m high consisting of **cross-stratified** breccias and sandstones. **Laminated**, well-sorted 2-10mm beds of fine sandstone are interbedded with impersistent beds of poorly sorted breccias showing no structure. A prominent **clast** of andesite lava in one breccia bed is over 25 cm in length (Figure 3). There is considerable small-scale faulting cutting off and disrupting beds. An exploration of the summit of Little Round How will reveal complex faulting, slumping and **cross-bedding** in the breccias. Beds of tiny (up to peanut size) ash-coated volcanic fragments (volcanic **lapilli**) may be found.

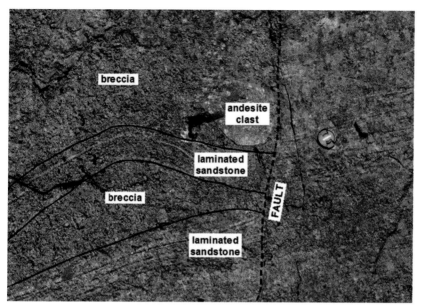

Figure 3. Breccias and laminated sandstones at Little Round How (Locality 5) with an outsize clast of andesitic lava. Beds are cut off by a small fault (dotted line). The lens cap is 62 mm in diameter. (Photo H. Tuffen)

The Round How breccias may have been formed when detritus from the andesite lavas was washed into a lake and combined with the ash and lapilli which had formed in explosive interactions between lava and lake water.

Locality 5 (NY 2069 1324) is where the path skirts the northern edge of Little Round How. Just off the path, the north face shows clast-supported breccias of andesitic lava juxtaposed with large areas of well-bedded pebbly sandstones and breccias. Bedded sandstones fill the gaps between the andesite lava clasts. This may indicate that the chilled, **autobrecciated** surface of the lava was invaded by water-lain sediments.

Locality 6 (NY 2127 1360) is a small, disused quarry to the northwest of Hopper Quarry. From Little Round How follow the path across

Dubs Bottom, pass the climbing hut and continue east-northeast along the quarry track for 500m until you reach Hopper Quarry on the left (north) side. Follow the track that bears left for 200m until you reach a small quarry. The blue-grey sedimentary rocks mined here vary from massive and poorly sorted breccias to well-sorted, laminated siltstones. These are volcanic in origin and were formed when vigorously erupting andesitic volcanoes dumped huge quantities of ash and lava fragments into a nearby lake. The breccias were deposited by gravity flows, whereas the siltstones were deposited from dilute suspension. **Rip-up clasts** and traction marks indicate that sediment supply was very rapid. Make your way to the end of a raised path on the right hand (eastern) side of the quarry, where you will find a ~4 m high outcrop on the right hand side (Figure 4).

Figure 4. The outcrop at Locality 6, showing the peperitic contact between the base of an andesite sill (top right) and the Honister Slates (bottom left).

(Photo H. Tuffen)

The lower part of the outcrop consists of blue-grey Honister slates. The prominent contact with the overlying dark grey brecciated lava is a peperitic contact between an andesitic sill and the Honister slates. The dark, locally **vesicular** andesite lava is brecciated where it contacts the sediments and the clasts have extremely irregular edges. This brecciation indicates how the lava was fragmenting as it contacted the waterlogged sediments, generating steam. The clasts are surrounded by homogenised sediment, often brilliant blue in colour, whose bedding has been destroyed by the invading lava. This may indicate that the sediment was waterlogged when the lava invaded and the formation of steam turned the sediment into a mobile fluid! Notice how this contact contrasts with that on Little Round How (Locality 5) where the brecciated andesite was cold when the infilling sediments were deposited. Here the opposite happened, with the wet sediment being invaded by very hot lava.

Locality 7 (NY 2149 1365) is a group of standing stones on either side of the track leading eastwards from Hopper Quarry towards Honister Pass. They currently include a number of exceptional examples of peperitic lavas, although the stones may change in the coming years. Clouds of extremely irregular, locally jigsaw-fit clasts of andesite are suspended in disrupted sediments (Figure 5) and many andesite clasts contain a large proportion of vesicles filled with homogenised sediment or minerals such as calcite.

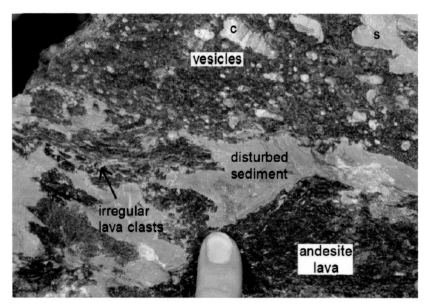

Figure 5. A typical peperitic contact between andesitic lava (dark) and Honister slates, showing disturbed, homogenised sediment(s) and irregular lava clasts with calcite-filled vesicles (c).
(Photo H.Tuffen)

From the standing stones leave the track and traverse southwards across the moorland (no path) to reach the old quarry tramway used on the way out. Alternatively continue down the track but beware large quarry vehicles which may not see you.

Locality 8 (NY 2247 1354) is the Honister Slate Mine, where there are superb polished slabs on display showing beautiful sedimentary structures in the Honister slate. There are several daily visits to the extensive levels cut into Fleetwith Pike.

Walk Number 16

Borrowdale Valley

by Judy Suddaby

Purpose	To look for evidence of igneous activity and how the Ice Age modified the landscape.

Practical Details

Starting point	Rosthwaite NT car park (NY 257 247).
Walk description	Moderate: Approx. 9km. Mainly fell walking paths at low level.
Map	1:25 000 OL4 The English Lakes North western area.
Public transport	Bus from Keswick.
Public toilets	Rosthwaite and Seatoller car parks and near Seathwaite public telephone box.
Refreshments	Rosthwaite and, depending on season, Seatoller and Seathwaite.

GEOLOGICAL SETTING

Borrowdale Volcanic Group rocks dominate this landscape. No volcanic peaks or craters remain, 450 million years of changes having occurred since they formed. The latest changes were the effects of glaciation.

EXCURSION DESCRIPTION

From the car park turn right to follow the track to the river, then downstream, and across 'New Bridge'. Turn left to two wooden bridges and cross the stile between them. Follow the tributary stream as far as open pasture. Bear left along the wall, aiming for the gate into the northernmost part of Johnny Wood. At the footpath within the wood, turn right, continue out onto open fell and up alongside Scaleclose Gill. Just before this path descends into the gill take the grassy path forking left still uphill. Over the ladder stile follow the faint path southwestwards (See Figure 1).

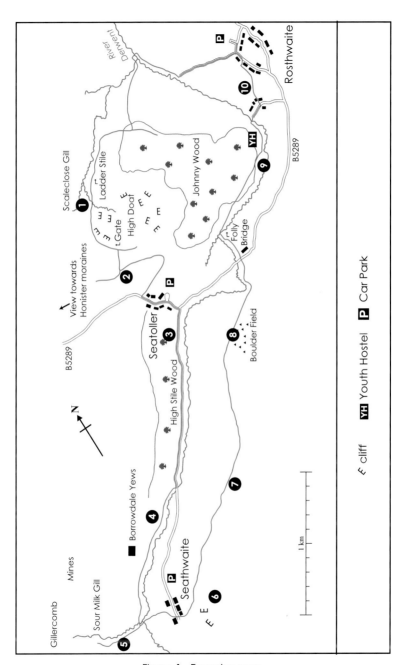

Figure 1. Excursion map.

137

Locality 1 (NY 245 146) is 150m after the ladder stile. Look for a small stream cutting through **glacial drift** and exposing loose stones. Crags 120m to the left are formed from grey **andesite,** also seen further along where exposed rock has been smoothed by ice. At a rocky knoll 20m to the left of the path, is the fine panorama down valley northwards to Castle Crag. This prominent mid-valley feature would, at the height of glacial activity, have been buried within the ice. The knoll upon which you are standing is formed partly from andesitic **lava** and partly from **tuff**. The former is fine grained but with large (1-2mm) aligned crystals of **feldspar**, which stand out because they resist weathering. The tuff shows **bedding** suggesting the ash was deposited in water. Continue southeast (left) of the wall and turn right through the first gate. Notice an ice-smoothed crag, across a small pool to the left of the path.

Locality 2 (NY 244 143) is 200m downhill southwest of the gate, on a wider track. Look up-valley to the right and notice hummocky **moraines** at Honister. These are probably deposits of the last local ice advance (the Lock Lomond **Stadial**) about 10,000 years ago, a mere blink of an eyelid in geological time. Staying on this wider track go left towards Seatoller. Notice, at the trackside, glacial drift over bedrock and obvious glacial polishing of the rock, an andesitic lava. Pale 2mm feldspar crystals are visible on some surfaces. These lavas were caught up in the same **regional metamorphism** as the tuffs forming Honister slates but because they are crystalline did not acquire a **slaty cleavage**. A gatepost along the track is of green Borrowdale slate (regionally metamorphosed tuff). Lakeland tuff is much used and valued for construction and ornamental use. The Yew Tree café floor in Seatoller is flagged with superb examples. After the gate, keep right where the paths diverge and continue downhill. A short walk through Seatoller brings you to a right turn, signposted Seathwaite.

Locality 3 (NY 244 135) A short distance along this road, look left at the bouldery **lateral moraine** across the valley. Thorneythwaite Farm stands on raised ground that is a **terminal moraine** left behind after the Pleistocene ice melted. At Seathwaite Bridge, turn through two gates on your right onto the grassy track beside the river. The second gatepost is of Honister slate.

Locality 4 (NY 238 126) Here the occasionally exposed bedrock, is composed of rocks of the Birker Fell Formation. These are mainly andesitic lavas and **sills**, with some tuffs and **breccias**. Look ahead to the skyline of Base Brown where inclined strata are tuffs and lavas of the later Borrowdale Volcanic Group formed during explosive eruptions.

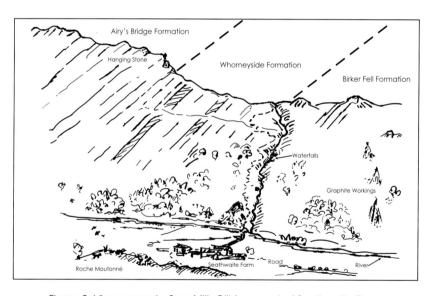

Figure 2. View across to Sour Milk Gill from east of Seathwaite Farm.
By courtesy of Dr. Alan Smith

The resistant lava forms cliffs; the weaker tuffs and breccias form gentler slopes, the contrast highlighted by differential erosion. Along the footpath, are boulders and crags with distinctive fine layering patterns. Some consist of tuff and others of volcanic ash that was 'reworked' in a watery environment to become **volcaniclastic** rocks.

After passing through a kissing gate, you can see, higher up the fell on the right, the remains of **graphite** (also known as wad or plumbago) mines (See Figure 2). Do not enter the mine workings which are dangerous. The spoil heaps rarely yield specimens. The origin of this unique ore-body has bewildered geologists for many years. It was certainly a valuable commodity in the heyday of mining operations from the mid-1500s to the late-1800s. Graphite has various uses, best known of which is as pencil 'lead' as demonstrated in the Pencil Museum in Keswick.

Locality 5 (NY 233 123) Go a few hundred metres up the Sour Milk Gill footpath over an unusual ladder-stile, and divert to the obvious Seathwaite Slabs on your left (see Figure 3). On south dipping exposed bedding planes are examples of the Whorneyside Formation, the product of very violent volcanism. Look for thick layers of air-fall tuff and an excellent variety of volcaniclastic sediments, some of them waterlain, displaying ripple marks, **current bedding** and perhaps **rip-up clasts.** A lower slab is breccia with a large boulder set in angular fragments of volcanic dust. The footpath has been remade using slabs, some of which have interesting fine layering. You might find mini-**fault** lines where damp volcanic mud slumped. Geologists draw parallels here with present day features on the flanks of Mount St. Helens. These slabs suggest colossal floods occurred during Ordovician explosive episodes. Imagine destructive lahars (mud flows) on the slopes of Borrowdale volcanoes and rivers carrying volcanic debris, eventually settling in lakes, or a sea.

Figure 3. View from Seathwaite Slabs looking south.
a: lava flow, b: fault guided streams, c: bedding in tuff
(Photo S. Beale)

Sour Milk Gill tumbles from Gillercomb, a hanging valley. During the Pleistocene Stage, Borrowdale was over-deepened by the main valley glacier compared with the valley of the Gillercomb glacier. Thus after the last ice retreat, the tributary valley was left relatively high. Notice, across the valley stream-gullies on the west facing fell-side exploiting weaknesses caused by faults (see Figure 3).

Descend along the footpath to enter Seathwaite via the gate under the arch. Turn left, then right (past the phone box and toilets), then right again to reach the signpost. Here turn left towards Thorneythwaite.

Locality 6 (NY 233 123). After about 100m, the Thorneythwaite footpath goes left through a kissing gate. However, continue 50m further to the right of the wall, to find the 0.5m andesitic **volcanic bomb,** which caused an obvious depression in the volcanic dust when it landed. The 'bomb' with its prominent drill hole is exposed in tuff about 10m from the wall, 1m up the left end of a north-facing crag (See Figure 4). It tells us that the Borrowdale volcano, the centre of which was probably some distance away, blasted through its lava cone with enormous force to eject such a large fragment.

Figure 4. Volcanic bomb causing depression in the tuff.
(Photo T. Blanchard)

This crag is one side of a **roche moutonnée,** a mid-valley feature smoothed by glacier on its up-ice side but left craggy on its down-ice side. From the top of it you can savour the valley structure: its gills, **alluvial fans** and rock formations. The smooth U-shape of the valley is typical of glaciated mountain valleys formed when ice pushing downstream cut off the spurs previously separating tributary streams. Eventually the ice melted leaving a terminal moraine at Thorneythwaite Farm, ponding back water to form a temporary lake. Sediments deposited in the lake filled hollows in the valley bottom, creating today's flat valley floor.

Return to the kissing-gate and proceed through it northwards, initially following several indistinct cairns across a field.

Locality 7 (NY 242 126) Stream-gullies on the west-facing fell-side are cutting down along weaknesses caused by faults. Proceeding northeastwards along the Allerdale Ramble footpath, you cross evidence of the fault lines at streams where bedrock has been reddened by iron-rich mineralising fluids, mostly **hematite.** These fluids seeped along fault lines during mountain building activity.

Locality 8 (NY 246 130) Here are the splendid boulder fields seen from Locality 3. The smaller particles from the lateral moraine were washed away leaving the heavier boulders behind. You now have a better view of the Gillercomb hanging valley, Base Brown and Sour Milk Gill. At Strands Bridge the footpath crosses the B5289 to reach Folly Bridge in less than 200m. Cross this and turn right towards Longthwaite. The path passes through the southeast part of Johnny Wood to the river.

Locality 9 (NY 255 142) is at the river, where the path now becomes tricky as it crosses a sloping andesite outcrop. On the opposite bank is an excellent vertical section of a terminal moraine. The unsorted particles of many shapes, sizes and origins show that this bank material was transported and deposited by ice rather than by water. (Water would have sorted the particles according to density and size.) It is the westernmost of the three arc-shaped moraines of Rosthwaite that date from the late Pleistocene glaciations.

The path continues through YHA grounds to join the road across the river. 100m after the bridge take the footpath signposted to the left.

Locality 10 (NY 257 145) In the pastures, there are dry-stone walls with large boulders at their bases. Some of the boulders are of a variety of rocks e.g. **agglomerate** and basalt not andesite, the local bedrock. Such boulders are termed '**erratics**' and have been carried down-valley from their source by a glacial 'conveyor belt'. Near the end of the houses there is, on your right, a garden fence of slate and, on your left, a rocky knoll of the andesite bedrock abraded by glaciers. This is another roche moutonnée.   A much larger one,   The How, is in the middle of Rosthwaite. At the end of the field, pass through the gate, turn right, then left and follow the road to the car park.

Walk Number 17

Rocks and Minerals of the Newlands Valley

by Anthony Rigby

Purpose	To appreciate the geology and landscape. To view several old mines, identifying some of the more common minerals.

Practical Details

Starting Points	For Newlands Valley, the small car park by Chapel Bridge (NY 233 195). For Stoneycroft mine park by the roadside near the bridge at (NY 232 213) or near Barrow Mine (NY 233 217).
Walk Description	Newlands Valley approx. 10km of easy walk to Localities 1 and 2, (optional) steep climbs to Localities 3 (350m), 4 and 6 at the head of the valley. 1-2 km at Stoneycroft.
Maps	1: 25 000 OL4 The English Lakes, North western area. 1:50 000 Landranger 89 West Cumbria or 1:50 000 Landranger 90. Penrith, Keswick & Ambleside area. 1:50 000 British Geological Survey, Sheet 29 Keswick
Public Transport	No regular bus service.
Public Toilets	None.
Refreshments	Pubs in Braithwaite.
Other requirements	Warm, waterproof clothing and good foot wear, preferably boots. A x10 hand lens and pen knife are useful for identifying minerals.

Special Warning:- *Old mine workings are extremely dangerous and should not be entered under any circumstances. Keep a safe distance from shafts and open workings.*

GEOLOGICAL SETTING

The hills to the west of the upper Newlands Valley are relatively smooth in outline, composed of slumped **sedimentary** Skiddaw Group rocks formed around 475**Ma** in the Ordovician Period. Further east in the upper valley the hills near Eel Crags and Dale Head are craggy, consisting of Lower Borrowdale Volcanic Group rocks formed later in the Ordovician, overlying the Skiddaw Group sediments.

The Skiddaw Group rocks were deposited by **turbidity** currents (underwater currents of high velocity descending to the deep ocean floor) over a wide area in deep seas off a continent which lay south of the Equator (see Introduction). Particle sizes in these sediments vary from fine grained mudstones (**metamorphosed** to **slate**) to coarse grained **conglomerates**. The volcanic rocks include both lavas and **tuffs** (hardened volcanic ash, the product of violent eruptions) and form a line of cliffs which gradually descend from north to south on the east side of Newlands.

Much later, base metal **veins** were **intruded** in two distinct phases along lines of weakness, usually **faults**. The older veins, of Devonian age, carried sulphides of copper, iron and arsenic. These trend east to west. The younger, of Carboniferous age, trend north to south and carry sulphides of lead and zinc. It is believed that these veins were formed by **hydrothermal** fluids, circulating through the rocks at high temperatures and driven by a major heat source derived from a large **granitic batholith**. Gravity surveys indicate that such a large intrusion exists at a relatively shallow depth beneath Lakeland.

The Newlands valley has been **glaciated** which explains its straight steep sides and flat floor with glacial **till** in places. Tributary valleys, where the ice was thinner and did not erode as much as the deeper ice in Newlands, "hang" in the west of the valley between Hindscarth and Dale Head.

EXCURSION DESCRIPTION

Walk 100m east from the Chapel Bridge car park to the bridleway which you follow south up the Newlands valley (Figure 1). Walk west across the footbridge (NY 230 183).

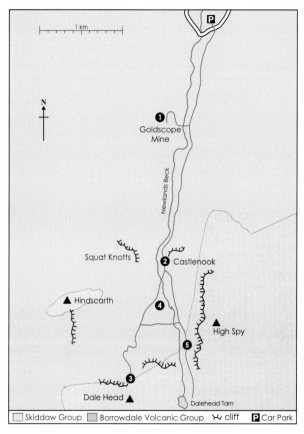

Figure 1.   Sketch map of the Newlands Valley.

Locality 1 is Goldscope Mine (NY 229 185), Figure 1, the famous and most productive series of workings for lead and copper in the Buttermere Formation (Skiddaw Group).   These rocks **dip** steeply. Our walk visits the large waste dumps on its eastern slope, where there is just one **adit**, the Grand Adit. which dates from 1566 and was started by German miners working for Queen Elizabeth 1. These men had great skill in tunnelling into rock, using hand tools as this was before the days of gunpowder. Higher up in the crags are slit-like workings in the veins where flecks of **pyrite** can still be seen in the rock. All these workings are at least of Elizabethan age. The ore extracted was **chalcopyrite** (a copper sulphide). The vein underground, over 2m wide in places, was extremely rich with some silver being extracted during smelting. The German miners installed an underground water wheel to raise the ore and to drain the mine. Towards the end of the 16th Century the mine was abandoned. Much later when the copper adit was being driven forward in 1852 a massive lead vein was struck underground. This vein was over 4m wide in places with massive ribs of solid **galena** (lead sulphide) over 1m wide. This bonanza lasted for 12 years, producing 5,000 tons of lead ore and yielding 22,000 ounces of silver. The mine eventually closed in 1920.

Figure 2. Looking west to the Goldscope Mine.
(Photo F. Lawton)

Even today these dumps are toxic to many plants. (See Figure 2). The rusty colour of the lower dumps is due to the oxidation of copper waste while the upper dumps are grey due to their lead content. Lower down on the tips the gangue (waste) minerals like **quartz** are common but few samples remain of the ore minerals; chalcopyrite (copper), arsenopyrite (arsenic sulphide), galena (lead) and **sphalerite** (zinc sulphide).

Return to the bridleway and walk 1.5km south to the next old mine, Castlenook.

Locality 2 is the old Castlenook mine (NY 227 170) situated below a crag descending from Maiden Moor. The rocks, which were originally muds and silts, have been altered by metamorphism and are now finely bedded, distinctively laminated **shales** which dip steeply south. They are part of the Buttermere Formation. The mine worked a rich vein at depth during the 19th Century. The upper adit has a 5-10m wide exposure of the vein, barren like the tips. To reach the next locality cross in turn Newlands Beck, Far and Near Tongue Gills, to follow a steep zig-zag path to the workings

Locality 3, is the old Dalehead copper mine (NY 224 155). This mine also dates back to at least Elizabethan times. Some colourful pieces, which can be found on an old hand dressing floor near a ruined bothy, are secondary minerals formed when the vein was deeply weathered near the surface. This upper part of the vein was the gossan (oxidised compounds), formed when chemical action over time altered the primary sulphide ores. These secondary minerals often have a high metallic content and were commercially valuable. The green coloured copper minerals here include **malachite** (a carbonate), chryscolla (a silicate) and brochantite (a sulphate). Bornite, the peacock copper ore, was the main primary ore mineral worked on this vein. There were three adits on this vein, two in the Buttermere Formation slates and the other in the younger volcanic rocks. As you return, turn east (right) when you are in line with an open vein which you follow east across Newlands Beck.

Locality 4 is the old Longwork mine (NY 228 162), Figure 3. It is an aptly named Elizabethan working with its intermittent but spectacularly exposed open vein stretching 300m west to east. This is in Skiddaw Group rocks dipping steeply. It was briefly reworked between 1919 and 1922. Chalcopyrite and malachite were the main ores but very little remains on the spoil heaps. A compact mound of waste remains below the western end of the openwork, just above Far Tongue Gill.

Continue south up the path, steeper and less distinct now. There are a wide range of volcanic boulders fallen from Eel Crag east of the stream. **Breccias** dominate, a particularly striking type has matrix supported **clasts** up to 10cm long with similar size pieces of finely bedded volcanic sediments in the same block. **Vesicular** lava (with holes formed where gases in hot lava escaped) with strikingly green later infills, are also present.

Figure 3. Looking west along the Longwork vein.
(Photo F. Lawton)

Locality 5 (NY 239 158) is the main waterfall by the steep footpath up to Dalehead Tarn.   This is the highest of a series of small falls with plunge pools and potholes, with the stone "drill bits" used to excavate round hollows up to 50cm deep still in place.   There is a possible contact between the Skiddaw Group beds and the volcanic rocks just east of the main waterfall.   West of the beck the laminated shales **strike** north to south and dip steeply eastwards, quite a contrast with the east to west strike of similar rocks by the Longwork vein.   Newlands Beck appears to follow the strike of these shales intermittently for 200-300m.   Return to Chapel Bridge.

Locality 6 is Stoneycroft Mine, (NY 233 213) To reach this drive up the steep lane to the Buttermere-Braithwaite road turn right (east) and continue for 1½ km to Stoneycroft Bridge.   If there is no parking there continue to Uzzicar and walk back 1½ km along the old mine track immediately below Barrow mountain.   Stoneycroft Mine is an ancient, small lead mine (Figure 4).

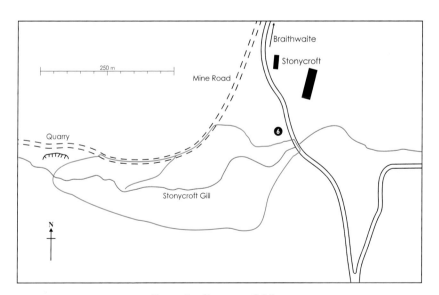

Figure 4.   Stoneycroft Mine.

Look down from the bridge over Stonycroft Gill at the exposures of thinly bedded/laminated Buttermere Formation shales in the ravine. Then walk up the steep ground north of the beck above the gorse to join the mine road near a manhole cover. As you do so you cross rock cut leats up to 1½ m deep. Turn right for about 10-20m along the mine road to view outcrops in and above the track. These are fine grained siltstones and mudstones with many tight, angular Z-shaped slump folds up to 1m in amplitude.

Continue west (the opposite direction) for about 50m to descend a path to view mining remains in and near the stream between (NY 231 212) and (NY 228 212). These include a stream diversion, adits and the site of a former smelter, now obscured by a small, covered reservoir. Return to the mine road just below which colourful samples of smelter waste may be found. Walk about 400m west along the mine road before following a path down to the gill. At (NY 227 210), 2-3m above the beck is a small quarry with thicker beds of coarser material than you have seen so far at Stoneycroft. These are parallel and cross laminated greywackes, (coarse, poorly sorted sandstones of a variety of origins), interbedded with mudstones and siltstones. The greywackes may represent **proximal turbidity** currents depositing coarser material on the deep water muds and silts. These original sediments are now preserved as beds of varying thickness. Cross the stream and return to the metalled road along a footpath running along the contour south of the stream. This path gives a panoramic view of the line of the chimney flue of the smelter and the network of leats you crossed earlier.

GLOSSARY

Accretionary lapilli: spherical pea size volcanic pellets with concentric layers formed from damp ash in steam rich eruptions.

Acid: describes igneous rocks rich in silica (SiO_2 more than 63%).

Adit: gently sloping entrance to a mine.

Agglomerate: rock composed of poorly sorted volcanic fragments.

Alluvial fan: material deposited by a stream when there is a sudden decrease in velocity due to change in gradient.

Amphibole: silicate mineral rich in iron and magnesium occurring in many igneous and metamorphic rocks.

Andesite: usually grey to blue, fine grained igneous rock (often lava) of intermediate chemical composition (around 60% silica).

Arête: steep sided knife edge ridge between corries in glaciated uplands.

Ash-flow: hot, highly concentrated flow of volcanic fragments less than 2mm diameter.

Augite: dark green to black mineral, rich in iron and magnesium, found in basalts and gabbros.

Aureole: area around an intrusion where rocks have been altered by thermal metamorphism.

Autobrecciated: where the crust of a viscous lava fragments as the lava continues to flow.

Barite: barium sulphate, usually a creamy colour mineral, often platy which occurs in mineral veins. Can be scratched by steel, noticeably heavy (high specific gravity) and brittle.

Basalt: a common, dark coloured, very fine grained, basic (less than 53% silica) igneous rock. Usually a lava.

Batholith: a very large igneous intrusion, cutting country rock.

Bed: a distinct layer within sedimentary rocks.

Bedding plane: separates one bed from another.

Biotite: a platy brown coloured mineral rich in iron and magnesium. (A type of mica).

Bioturbated: a sediment which has been disturbed by the action of organisms.

Brachiopod: a two shelled marine invertebrate.

Breccia: rock composed of angular broken fragments up to 64 mm in diameter.

Brockram: a Cumbrian name for sedimentary breccia.

BP: before present time.

Calcite: calcium carbonate ($CaCO_3$), the most common carbonate mineral. The principal component of limestone.

Caldera: a very large volcanic crater formed by the collapse of a volcanic cone.

Chalcopyrite: the most important copper ore, brassy or golden yellow. $CuFeS_2$.

Cirque: see corrie.

Clast: a rock fragment.

Cleavage: plane of weakness in a rock, caused by platy crystals being aligned during rock deformation.

Clint: a joint bounded, near rectangular slab of bare hard limestone, usually horizontal.

Conglomerate: rounded clasts over 2 mm diameter cemented to form a rock.

Contact zone: an area around an intrusion where the pre-existing rocks have been altered by heat.

Corrie: a deep armchair shaped hollow gouged by a glacier sometimes with a circular lake or tarn. Sometimes moraine dammed.

Cross-bedding: the internal structure of a sedimentary rock formed by the accumulation of ripples, dunes etc. It is usually recognised in cross section by bedding planes cutting across one another. Also called current bedding and cross-stratification.

Dacite: a light coloured, fine grained, acidic (over 63% silica) igneous rock, often a lava.

Devensian: the last major ice advance, 115-10,000 BP

Diagenesis: processes, (chemical, physical and/or biological) by which unconsolidated sediment becomes rock.

Dip: the inclination of a planar body, measured from the horizontal

Dolerite: a medium grained igneous rock similar in composition to basalt. It usually occurs in shallow intrusions.

Drift: material deposited by ice sheets or glaciers.

Dolomite: a) mineral. calcium magnesium carbonate, common in altered limestones and mineral veins.
b) rock. A limestone rich in dolomite.

Drumlin: long, oval, streamlined hill, of glacial drift, with one steep and one gentle end. Normally they occur in groups and parallel the direction of ice movement.

Dyke: vertical or steeply inclined sheet of igneous material cross cutting country rock.

Erratic: a rock carried by ice and deposited away from its outcrop.

Esker: an embankment like feature, formed from the deposits of a subglacial stream which flowed under high pressure.

Eutaxitic: the texture formed by the streaking out of glassy shards and other material in an incandescent fast moving volcanic cloud.

Fault: a displacement of one block of rock relative to another.

Fault plane; the surface along which the rocks moved relative to one another. This can be in any orientation. **Strike-slip fault**: movement is dominantly horizontal. **Normal fault**: movement is mainly vertical.

Feldspar: A complex aluminium silicate mineral making up 60% of the earth's crust. Essential constituent of igneous rocks.

Fluvioglacial: streams within, under or beside ice and the material they deposit.

Flute mark: a tongue shaped scar cut into mud by a turbulent flow of water. Often recognised as a cast of the scar.

Fold: the bending of strata due to compression; **plunging fold:** a fold inclined from the horizontal.

Foreset bed: the steeply dipping front surface in cross-bedding; the front of an advancing bed form.

Frost wedging: fracturing of rock as cracks expand when water freezes.

Gabbro: a dark, coarse grained igneous rock, chemically similar to basalt. Forms in large deep intrusions.

Galena: Lead sulphide (PbS) The most important lead ore. Grey, silvery when fresh, heavy (high specific gravity) often showing cubic cleavage.

Glacial drift: material deposited by ice.

Glaciofluvial: see fluvioglacial.

Granite: coarse grained igneous rock, rich in silica. This rock has quartz, feldspar and mica crystals.

Granophyre: a medium grained igneous rock, chemically similar to granite but with intergrown quartz and feldspar crystals.

Graphite: an amorphous form of pure carbon.

Greywacke: poorly sorted coarse grained sandstone often with angular fragments.

Half-graben: a long, linear depression dropped down on one side by a normal fault.

Hanging valley: a tributary valley in a glaciated landscape in which the main valley has been much more deeply excavated.

Hematite: a very common iron oxide, sometimes forming iron ore. Fe_2O_3. Heavy (high specific gravity), brittle and dark red, often stains.

Hornfels: A hard splintery rock resulting from the baking of sedimentary rock.

Hydrothermal alteration: change in rock caused by passage of hot mineralised solutions. Also hydrothermal fluids.

Hypersaline: aqueous solutions with a very high content of salts.

Iapetus: The proto Atlantic Ocean that existed before the Caledonian mountain building episode.

Igneous: rock formed from magma.

Ignimbrite: a deposit from an incandescent volcanic ash flow, including fragments and molten globules, preserved as dark, glassy streaks. Indicates a very violent eruption.

Interstadial: a short interval of warming during an Ice Age.

Intrusion: igneous rocks pushed into pre-existing rock. Also intruded.

Inlier: older rocks completely surrounded by younger.

Joint: crack in rocks formed when igneous rocks cool, or when water is expelled from sedimentary rocks.

Kame: steep sided mound of bedded sand and gravel associated with the melting of stagnant ice.

Kettle hole: hollow in the surface of glacial drift. This is formed when a block of ice is buried in drift and later melts.

Lahar: catastrophic mudflow on the flank of a volcano.

Laminations: very fine layering of sediments.

Lava: molten material extruded by a volcano. It forms a fine grained rock.

Lithification: the processes of changing unconsolidated sediments into rock.

Load and flame structure: upward pointing projection of mud into overlying sands.

Ma: million years ago.

Magma: molten material formed by partial melting of the earth's crust or mantle.

Malachite: copper carbonate $Cu_2(CO)_3$ often bright green.

Metamorphism: Regional metamorphism. Process by which rocks are regionally altered by high pressure and temperature, usually in a mountain forming context. **Thermal** (or **Contact**) metamorphism. Process by which rocks are altered by contact with a hot igneous intrusion.

Metaquartzite: a metamorphic rock consisting mainly of quartz, originally a quartz rich sandstone.

Mica and **Micaceous:** a very common platy mineral consisting of silicates bonded in sheets. 2 main types, dark **biotite** and lighter coloured **muscovite**.

Moraine: sediment deposited by ice or ice and water. The term also applies to the resulting landform: terminal at the end of the ice, lateral at the side.

Muscovite: a complex platy white coloured aluminium silicate often rich in potassium. A very common mineral in igneous and metamorphic rocks. (A type of mica).

Normal fault: see "fault".

Orogeny: a mountain building episode.

Orthoclase: potassium rich, sometimes pink coloured feldspar.

Overlap: the successive increase in area of younger sedimentary beds, often above an unconformity.

Palaeocurrent: currents active in the geological past whose traces can be recognized in the rocks.

Peperite: a breccia of sedimentary clasts and magma particles, formed where magma intrudes into or lave flows over wet sediments. Also **Peperitic**.

Plagioclase: sodium or calcium-rich white coloured feldspar.

Plate: a very large mass of rigid crust which moves across the globe as a unit.

Playa: intermontain desert basin from which water evaporates quickly.

Plunging fold: see fold.

Pyrite: iron sulphide (FeS_2). A hard, brassy, metallic mineral often showing cubic cleavage.

Pyroclastic: volcanic particles produced by explosive activity.

Quartz: silica dioxide (SiO_2). White or colourless glassy hard mineral. Cannot be scratched with a knife. The commonest mineral.

Rhyolite: an acidic lava (i.e. rich in silica).

Rip-up clasts: particles removed from an underlying bed into the bed above.

Roches moutonnées: a mound like landform of glacial erosion with a smooth streamlined up valley surface and a cliffed, steep, irregular down valley slope.

Rugose coral: palaeozoic coral with wrinkled outer surfaces.

Sedimentary: rocks formed from deposits on the earth's surface.

Shale: bedded hardened silt/mud.

Sill: an igneous intrusion generally concordant (parallel) to the bedding of the rocks it intrudes.

Siltstone: a sedimentary rock with clasts intermediate in size between mud and sand.

Slate: rock that splits (cleaves) along parallel closely spaced planes. The result of regional metamorphism.

Slaty cleavage: see slate.

Stadial: a time of increasing cold or ice advance within an Ice Age.

Strike: the direction of an imaginary horizontal line on an inclined rock layer. (right angles to the dip).

Subduction: the destruction of a plate or part of one at a convergent plate margin (where plates meet).

Syncline: a down fold with younger rocks outcropping at its centre.

Tectonic: associated with mountain building processes involving major earth movements – usually the movement of one tectonic plate relative to another.

Thermal metamorphism: – see metamorphism.

Till: sediments deposited by ice.

Trace fossils: structures left by the action of ancient organisms.

Tuff: hardened volcanic ash.

Turbidite: sediment deposited by a subaqueous current triggered by an individual event e.g. an earthquake. **Distal turbidites**: generally fine grained sediment deposited far from the source area. **Proximal turbidites**: generally coarse grained sediment deposited close to the source.

Unconformity: a break in the stratigraphic record reflecting a time of erosion and/or non-deposition. Also **unconformable.**

Vein: a cross-cutting, often steeply inclined mineralised body.

Vesicular: a lava rich in cavities which were filled with gases at the time of eruption. Also **vesicles**.

Volcaniclastic: fragments formed by volcanic activity.

Volcanic bomb: a clot of lava, ejected while viscous, that solidifies before it lands.

Weathering: the breakdown of rocks in situ by natural processes - physical, chemical and biological.

MUSEUMS IN CUMBRIA

Haig Colliery Mining Museum, Solway Road, Kells, Whitehaven CA28 9BG
Tel. 01946-599949   Admission free.
Artifacts and history of coal mining in West Cumbria.
www.haigpit.com.co.uk

Kendal Natural History and Archaeology Museum. Station Road, Kendal, Cumbria
LA9 6BT
Tel. 01539 721374   Admission charge.
Natural History Gallery contains a wealth of fossils, local minerals and rock types.
www.kendalmuseum.org.uk

Keswick Mining Museum, Otley Road, Keswick CA12 5LE
Tel. 017687 80055   Admission charge.
A museum of Cumbrian mining from the Stone Age to the modern day. Includes a
good selection of books, covering mining, geology, minerals and related subjects.
www.keswickminingmuseum.co.uk

Keswick Museum and Art Gallery, Station Road, Keswick CA12 4NF
Tel. 017687-73263   Admission free.
Home of the famous 'Singing Stones'. A small local museum with a collection of
local rocks, fossils and minerals. Limited opening, please check before going.
www.allerdale.gov.uk/keswick-museum/

Penrith Museum, Middlegate, Penrith CA11 7PT
Tel. 01768 865105 Admission free.
A small museum with exhibits on the history, geology and archaeology
of Penrith and the Eden Valley.
www.eden.gov.uk/main.asp?page=126

Ruskin Museum, Coniston LA21 8DU
Tel. 015394 41164   Admission charge.
Concerns the life of John Ruskin with exhibits on geology and the coppermines.
www.ruskinmuseum.com

Threlkeld Quarry and Mining Museum, Threlkeld, Nr. Keswick CA12 4TT
Tel. 017687 79202   Admission charge.
Situated in the old quarry at Threlkeld, four miles east of Keswick. Geological
map with specimens. Information on quarrying and mining and examples of
vintage machinery.
Offers underground tours. Limited opening – please check before going.
www.threlkeldminingmuseum.co.uk

The Beacon, West Strand, Whitehaven CA28 7LY
Tel. 01946 592502   Admission charge.
Specializes in local history and coal mining.
www.copelandbc.gov.uk/ms/www/thebeacon/The-Museum.htm

Tullie House Museum, Castle Street, Carlisle CA3 8TP
Tel. 01228 618718   Admission charge.
Excellent collection of local minerals and fossils.
Occasional displays of local geology.
www.tulliehouse.co.uk

Further Information on the Geology of Lakeland is available from the following organisations:

Cumberland Geological Society
www.cumberland-geol-soc.org.uk

Westmorland Geological Society
www.westmorlandgeolsoc.org.uk

Furness Geological Group
Email: cumbus@texco.net

Yorkshire Geological Group
www.yorksgeolsoc.org.uk

Open University Geological Society
www.ougs.org

Geologists Association
www.geologists.demon.co.uk

British Geological Survey
www.britishgeologicalsurvey.com

INDEX